It's another great book from CGP...

This book is for anyone doing the **AQA Level 1/Level 2 Certificate in Physics**.

It's got clear, concise revision notes covering everything you'll need to do well in the exams. What's more, we've included a **free** Online Edition so that you can revise on a computer or tablet — wherever you are.

How to get your free Online Edition

Just go to **cgpbooks.co.uk/extras** and enter this code...

3536 6374 8921 9534

By the way, this code only works for one person. If somebody else has used this book before you, they might have already claimed the Online Edition.

CGP — still the best! ☺

Our sole aim here at CGP is to produce the highest quality books — carefully written, immaculately presented and dangerously close to being funny.

Then we work our socks off to get them out to you — at the cheapest possible prices.

Contents

Published by CGP

From original material by Richard Parsons.

Editors:
Jane Ellingham, Matteo Orsini-Jones, Sam Pilgrim, Karen Wells, Charlotte Whiteley.

Contributors:
Paddy Gannon, Gemma Hallam, Jason Howell

ISBN: 978 1 84762 450 5

With thanks to Mark Edwards and Glenn Rogers for the proofreading.
With thanks to Anna Lupton and Laura Jakubowski for the copyright research.

Data used to construct stopping distance diagram on page 22 From the Highway Code.
© Crown Copyright re-produced under the terms of the Open Government licence
http://www.nationalarchives.gov.uk/doc/open-government-licence/

Groovy website: www.cgpbooks.co.uk

Printed by Elanders Ltd, Newcastle upon Tyne.
Jolly bits of clipart from CorelDRAW®

How Science Works

You need to know a few things about the scientific process. First up is how science works — or how a scientist's mad idea turns into a widely accepted theory.

Scientists Come Up with Hypotheses — Then Test Them

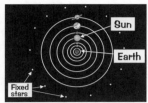

About 500 years ago, we still thought the Solar System looked like this.

1) Scientists try to explain things. Everything.

2) They start by observing something they don't understand — it could be anything, e.g. planets in the sky, a person suffering from an illness, what matter is made of... anything.

3) Then, they come up with a hypothesis — a possible explanation for what they've observed. Scientists can sometimes form a model too — a simplified description or representation of what's physically going on.

4) The next step is to test whether the hypothesis might be right or not — this involves gathering evidence (i.e. data from investigations).

5) The scientist uses the hypothesis to make a prediction — a statement based on the hypothesis that can be tested. They then carry out an investigation.

6) If data from experiments or studies backs up the prediction, you're one step closer to figuring out if the hypothesis is true.

Investigations include lab experiments and studies.

Other Scientists Will Test the Hypothesis Too

1) Other scientists will use the hypothesis to make their own predictions, and carry out their own experiments or studies.

2) They'll also try to reproduce the original investigations to check the results.

3) And if all the experiments in the world back up the hypothesis, then scientists start to think it's true.

4) However, if a scientist somewhere in the world does an experiment that doesn't fit with the hypothesis (and other scientists can reproduce these results), then the hypothesis is in trouble.

5) When this happens, scientists have to come up with a new hypothesis (maybe a modification of the old hypothesis, or maybe a completely new one).

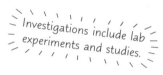

Then we thought it looked like this.

If Evidence Supports a Hypothesis, It's Accepted — for Now

1) If pretty much every scientist in the world believes a hypothesis to be true because experiments back it up, then it usually goes in the textbooks for students to learn.

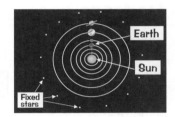

Now we think it's more like this.

2) Accepted hypotheses are often referred to as theories.

3) Our currently accepted theories are the ones that have survived this 'trial by evidence' — they've been tested many, many times over the years and survived (while the less good ones have been ditched).

4) However... they never, never become hard and fast, totally indisputable fact. You can never know... it'd only take one odd, totally inexplicable result, and the hypothesising and testing would start all over again.

You expect me to believe that — then show me the evidence...

If scientists think something is true, they need to produce evidence to convince others — it's all part of testing a hypothesis. One hypothesis might survive these tests, while others won't — it's how things progress. And along the way some hypotheses will be disproved — i.e. shown not to be true.

Your Data's Got To Be Good

Evidence is the key to science — but not all evidence is equally good.
The way evidence is gathered can have a big effect on how trustworthy it is...

Lab Experiments and Studies Are Better Than Rumour

See page 5 for more about fair tests and variables.

1) Results from experiments in laboratories are great. A lab is the easiest place to control variables so that they're all kept constant (except for the one you're investigating). This makes it easier to carry out a FAIR TEST.

2) For things that you can't investigate in the lab (e.g. climate) you conduct scientific studies. As many of the variables as possible are controlled, to make it a fair test.

3) Old wives' tales, rumours, hearsay, "what someone said", and so on, should be taken with a pinch of salt. Without any evidence they're NOT scientific — they're just opinions.

The Bigger the Sample Size the Better

1) Data based on small samples isn't as good as data based on large samples. A sample should be representative of the whole population (i.e. it should share as many of the various characteristics in the population as possible) — a small sample can't do that as well.

2) The bigger the sample size the better, but scientists have to be realistic when choosing how big. For example, if you were studying the health effects of mobile phone use it'd be great to study everyone in the UK (a huge sample), but it'd take ages and cost a bomb. Studying a thousand people is more realistic.

Evidence Needs to be Repeatable and Reproducible

You can have confidence in the results if they can be repeated (during the same experiment) AND other scientists can reproduce them too (in other experiments). If the results aren't repeatable or reproducible, you can't believe them.

> The data must be repeatable and reproducible by others.

If the results are repeatable and reproducible, they're said to be reliable.

EXAMPLE: In 1989, two scientists claimed that they'd produced 'cold fusion' (the energy source of the Sun — but without the big temperatures). It was huge news — if true, it would have meant cheap and abundant energy for the world... forever. However, other scientists just couldn't reproduce the results, so they couldn't be believed. And until they are, 'cold fusion' won't be accepted as fact.

Evidence Also Needs to Be Valid

> VALID means the data is repeatable, reproducible AND answers the original question.

EXAMPLE: DO POWER LINES CAUSE CANCER?
Some studies have found that children who live near overhead power lines are more likely to develop cancer. What they'd actually found was a correlation (relationship) between the variables "presence of power lines" and "incidence of cancer" — they found that as one changed, so did the other. But this evidence is not enough to say that the power lines cause cancer, as other explanations might be possible. For example, power lines are often near busy roads, so the areas tested could contain different levels of pollution from traffic. So these studies don't show a definite link and so don't answer the original question.

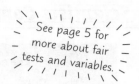

Repeat after me — repeatable and reproducible = great data...

By now you should have realised how important trustworthy evidence is (even more important than a good supply of spot cream). Unfortunately, you need to know loads more about fair tests and experiments — see p. 5-10.

Bias and Issues Created by Science

It isn't all hunky-dory in the world of science — there are some problems...

Scientific Evidence can be Presented in a Biased Way

1) People who want to make a point can sometimes present data in a biased way, e.g. they overemphasise a relationship in the data. (Sometimes without knowing they're doing it.)

2) There are all sorts of reasons why people might want to do this — for example...

- They want to keep the organisation or company that's funding the research happy. (If the results aren't what they'd like they might not give them any more money to fund further research.)
- Governments might want to persuade voters, other governments, journalists, etc.
- Companies might want to 'big up' their products. Or make impressive safety claims.
- Environmental campaigners might want to persuade people to behave differently.

Things can Affect How Seriously Evidence is Taken

1) If an investigation is done by a team of highly-regarded scientists it's sometimes taken more seriously than evidence from less well known scientists.

2) But having experience, authority or a fancy qualification doesn't necessarily mean the evidence is good — the only way to tell is to look at the evidence scientifically (i.e. is it valid).

3) Also, some evidence might be ignored if it could create political problems, or emphasised if it helps a particular cause.

EXAMPLE: Some governments were pretty slow to accept the fact that human activities are causing global warming, despite all the evidence. This is because accepting it means they've got to do something about it, which costs money and could hurt their economy. This could lose them a lot of votes.

Scientific Developments are Great, but they can Raise Issues

Scientific knowledge is increased by doing experiments. And this knowledge leads to scientific developments, e.g. new technologies or new advice. These developments can create issues though. For example:

Economic issues: Society can't always afford to do things scientists recommend (e.g. investing heavily in alternative energy sources) without cutting back elsewhere.

Social issues: Decisions based on scientific evidence affect people — e.g. should fossil fuels be taxed more highly (to invest in alternative energy)? Should alcohol be banned (to prevent health problems)? Would the effect on people's lifestyles be acceptable...

Environmental issues: Nuclear power stations can provide us with a reliable source of electricity, but disposing of the waste can lead to environmental issues.

Ethical issues: There are a lot of things that scientific developments have made possible, but should we do them? E.g. develop better nuclear weapons.

Trust me — I've got a BSc, PhD, PC, TV and a DVD...

We all tend to swoon at people in authority, but you have to ignore that fact and look at the evidence (just because someone has got a whacking great list of letters after their name doesn't mean the evidence is good). Spotting biased evidence isn't the easiest thing in the world — ask yourself 'Does the scientist (or the person writing about it) stand to gain something (or lose something)?' If they do, it's possible that it could be biased.

The Scientific Process

Science Has Limits

Science can give us amazing things — cures for diseases, space travel, heated toilet seats...
But science has its limitations — there are questions that it just can't answer.

Some Questions Are Unanswered by Science — So Far

1) We don't understand everything. And we never will. We'll find out more, for sure — as more hypotheses are suggested, and more experiments are done. But there'll always be stuff we don't know.

   > **EXAMPLES:**
   > * Today we don't know as much as we'd like about the impacts of global warming. How much will sea level rise? And to what extent will weather patterns change?
   > * We also don't know anywhere near as much as we'd like about the Universe. Are there other life forms out there? And what is the Universe made of?

2) These are complicated questions. At the moment scientists don't all agree on the answers because there isn't enough valid evidence.

3) But eventually, we probably will be able to answer these questions once and for all... All we need is more evidence.

4) But by then there'll be loads of new questions to answer.

Other Questions Are Unanswerable by Science

1) Then there's the other type... questions that all the experiments in the world won't help us answer — the "Should we be doing this at all?" type questions. There are always two sides...

2) Take space exploration. It's possible to do it — but does that mean we should?

3) Different people have different opinions.

> For example...
>
> Some people say it's a good idea... it increases our knowledge about the Universe, we develop new technologies that can be useful on Earth too, it inspires young people to take an interest in science, etc.
>
> Other people say it's a bad idea... the vast sums of money it costs should be spent on more urgent problems, like providing clean drinking water and curing diseases in poor countries. Others say that we should concentrate research efforts on understanding our own planet better first.

4) The question of whether something is morally or ethically right or wrong can't be answered by more experiments — there is no "right" or "wrong" answer.

5) The best we can do is get a consensus from society — a judgement that most people are more or less happy to live by. Science can provide more information to help people make this judgement, and the judgement might change over time. But in the end it's up to people and their conscience.

Chips or rice? — totally unanswerable by science...

Right — get this straight in your head — science can't tell you whether you should or shouldn't do something. That kind of thing is up to you and society to decide. There are tons of questions that science might be able to answer in the future — like how much sea level might rise due to global warming, what the Universe is made of and whatever happened to those pink stripy socks with Santa on that I used to have.

Designing Investigations

Real <u>scientists</u> need to know <u>how to plan</u> and <u>carry out</u> <u>scientific experiments</u>. Unluckily for you, those pesky examiners think <u>you</u> should be able to do the same — so you'll have <u>questions on experiments</u> in your exams. Don't worry though, these next seven pages have <u>loads of information</u> to help you out.

Investigations _Produce Evidence_ to _Support_ or _Disprove_ a _Hypothesis_

1) Scientists <u>observe</u> things and come up with <u>hypotheses</u> to explain them (see page 1).

2) To figure out whether a hypothesis might be correct or not you need to do an <u>investigation</u> to <u>gather some evidence</u>.

3) The first step is to use the hypothesis to come up with a <u>prediction</u> — a statement about what you <u>think will happen</u> that you can <u>test</u>.

4) For example, if the <u>hypothesis</u> is:

> "Spots are caused by picking your nose too much."

Then the <u>prediction</u> might be:

> "People who pick their nose more often will have more spots."

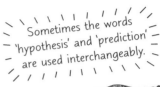
Sometimes the words 'hypothesis' and 'prediction' are used interchangeably.

5) Investigations are used to see if there are <u>patterns</u> or <u>relationships between two variables</u>. For example, to see if there's a pattern or relationship between the variables 'having spots' and 'nose picking'.

6) The investigation has to be a <u>FAIR TEST</u> to make sure the evidence is <u>valid</u>...

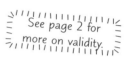
See page 2 for more on validity.

To Make an Investigation a _Fair Test_ You Have to _Control the Variables_

1) In a lab experiment you usually <u>change one variable</u> and <u>measure</u> how it affects the <u>other variable</u>.

> EXAMPLE: you might change only the angle of a slope and measure how it affects the time taken for a toy car to travel down it.

2) To make it a fair test <u>everything else</u> that could affect the results should <u>stay the same</u> (otherwise you can't tell if the thing you're changing is causing the results or not — the data won't be valid).

> EXAMPLE continued: you need to keep the slope length the same, otherwise you won't know if any change in the time taken is caused by the change in angle, or the change in length.

3) The variable you CHANGE is called the INDEPENDENT variable.

4) The variable you MEASURE is called the DEPENDENT variable.

5) The variables that you KEEP THE SAME are called CONTROL variables.

> EXAMPLE continued:
> Independent variable = angle of slope
> Dependent variable = time taken
> Control variable = length of slope

6) You can sometimes also include a CONTROL EXPERIMENT to make sure no other factors are affecting the result. This is an experiment that's kept under the <u>same conditions</u> as the rest of the investigation, but doesn't have anything done to it. This is so that you can see what happens when you don't change anything at all.

Designing Investigations

Trial Runs help Figure out the Range and Interval of Variable Values

1) It's a good idea to do a trial run (preliminary experiment) first — a quick version of the experiment.

2) Trial runs are used to figure out the range of variable values used in the proper experiment (the upper and lower limit). For example, if you can't accurately measure the change in the dependent variable at the upper values in the trial run, you might narrow the range in the proper experiment.

3) And trial runs can be used to figure out the interval (gaps) between the values too. The intervals can't be too small (otherwise the experiment would take ages), or too big (otherwise you might miss something).

4) Trial runs can also help you figure out whether or not your experiment is repeatable. E.g. if you repeat it three times and the results are all similar, the experiment is repeatable.

Slope example from previous page continued:
You might do trial runs at 20, 40, 60 and 80°. If the time taken is too short to accurately measure at 80°, you might narrow the range to 20-60°.

If using 20° intervals gives you a big change in time taken you might decide to use 10° intervals, e.g. 20, 30, 40, 50°...

It Can Be Hard to Control the Variables in a Study

It's important that a study is a fair test, just like a lab experiment. It's a lot trickier to control the variables in a study than in a lab experiment though (see previous page). Sometimes you can't control them all, but you can use a control group to help. This is a group of whatever you're studying (people, plants, lemmings, etc.) that's kept under the same conditions as the group in the experiment, but doesn't have anything done to it.

EXAMPLE: If you're studying the link between CT scans and thyroid cancer, you take one group of people who have had CT scans and another group (the control group) who haven't. Both groups should be of roughly the same age, live in the same area, have similar lifestyles etc. The control group is there to try to account for other local variables that might affect the chances of people developing thyroid cancer.

Investigations Can be Hazardous

1) A hazard is something that can potentially cause harm. Hazards include:

- Radioactivity, e.g. too much exposure can damage skin cells.
- Springs, e.g. a taut spring can become detached or snap, so you need to protect your eyes.
- Fire, e.g. an unattended Bunsen burner is a fire hazard.
- Electricity, e.g. faulty electrical equipment could give you a shock.

Hmm... Where did my bacteria sample go?

2) Scientists need to manage the risk of hazards by doing things to reduce them. For example:

- If you're stretching a metal spring using weights, make sure it's clamped firmly and that you don't apply too much force. This way it won't snap or flick up into your face.
- If you're using a Bunsen burner, stand it on a heat proof mat. This will reduce the risk of starting a fire.

You can find out about potential hazards by looking in textbooks, doing some internet research, or asking your teacher.

You won't get a trial run at the exam, so get learnin'...

All this info needs to be firmly lodged in your memory. Learn the names of the different variables — if you remember that the variable you chaNge is called the iNdependent variable, you can figure out the other ones.

Collecting Data

It's important to collect data that you can <u>trust</u> — data that's <u>repeatable</u>, <u>reproducible</u>, <u>accurate</u> and <u>precise</u>. Read on my intrepid friend...

Data Should be as Accurate and Precise as Possible

1) To show that results are repeatable, and so improve validity, readings should be repeated at least <u>three times</u> and a <u>mean</u> (average) calculated.

2) To make sure that results are reproducible you can cross check them by taking a <u>second set of readings</u> with <u>another instrument</u> (or a <u>different observer</u>).

3) Checking that results match with <u>secondary sources</u>, e.g. other studies, also increases the validity.

4) Data also needs to be ACCURATE. Really accurate results are <u>really close</u> to the <u>true answer</u>. The accuracy of the results usually depends on the <u>method</u> and the <u>equipment</u> used, e.g. when measuring <u>how long</u> a ball takes to roll down a slope, you should use a <u>stopwatch</u> to accurately measure the time.

5) Data also needs to be PRECISE. Precise results are ones where the data is <u>all really close</u> to the <u>mean</u> (i.e. not spread out).

Remember — to be valid, data has to be repeatable and reproducible (p. 2).

The Equipment has to be Right for the Job

1) The measuring equipment you use has to be <u>sensitive enough</u> to measure the changes being looked for. For example, if you need to measure changes of 1 ml you need to use a measuring cylinder that can measure in 1 ml steps — it'd be no good trying with one that only measures 10 ml steps.

2) The <u>smallest change</u> a measuring instrument can <u>detect</u> is called its RESOLUTION. E.g. some mass balances have a resolution of 1 g, some have a resolution of 0.1 g, and some are even more sensitive.

3) Also, equipment needs to be <u>calibrated</u> so that your data is <u>more accurate</u>. E.g. mass balances need to be set to zero before you start weighing things.

You Need to Look out for Errors and Anomalous Results

1) The results of an experiment will always <u>vary a bit</u> because of RANDOM ERRORS — tiny differences caused by things like <u>human errors</u> in <u>measuring</u>.

2) Their effect can be <u>reduced</u> by taking many readings and calculating the <u>mean</u>.

3) If the <u>same error</u> is made every time, it's called a SYSTEMATIC ERROR. For example, if you measured from the very end of your ruler instead of from the 0 cm mark every time, all your measurements would be a bit small.

Repeating the experiment in the exact same way and calculating an average won't correct a systematic error.

4) Just to make things more complicated, if a systematic error is caused by using <u>equipment</u> that <u>isn't zeroed properly</u> it's called a ZERO ERROR. For example, if a mass balance always reads 1 gram before you put anything on it, all your measurements will be 1 gram too heavy.

5) Some systematic errors can be <u>compensated</u> for if you know about them though, e.g. if your mass balance always reads 1 gram before you put anything on it you can subtract 1 gram from all your results.

6) Sometimes you get a result that <u>doesn't seem to fit in</u> with the rest at all.

7) These results are called ANOMALOUS RESULTS.

8) They should be <u>investigated</u> to find out what <u>caused them</u>. If you can work out what happened (e.g. something was measured wrong) you can <u>ignore</u> them when processing the results.

Park	No. of pigeons	No. of zebras
A	28	1
B	42	2
C	1127	0

Zero error — sounds like a Bruce Willis film...

Weirdly, data can be really <u>precise</u> but <u>not very accurate</u>, e.g. a fancy piece of lab equipment might give results that are precise, but if it's not calibrated properly those results won't be accurate.

Processing and Presenting Data

If you've got some results from an experiment, you might need to process and present them so you can look for patterns and relationships in them.

Data Needs to be Organised

1) Tables are dead useful for organising data.

2) If you have to draw a table use a ruler, make sure each column has a heading (including the units) and keep it neat and tidy.

3) You might be asked to describe the results in a table or pick out an anomalous result.

4) But tables aren't usually that great for showing patterns in data, so you might be asked to draw a graph.

You Might Have to Process Some Data

1) The repeats of an experiment should be used to calculate a mean (average). To do this ADD TOGETHER all the data values and DIVIDE by the total number of values in the sample.

2) You might also need to calculate the range (how spread out the data is). To do this find the LARGEST number and SUBTRACT the SMALLEST number from it.

Ignore anomalous results when calculating these.

EXAMPLE

Test tube	Repeat 1 (g)	Repeat 2 (g)	Repeat 3 (g)	Mean (g)	Range (g)
A	28	37	32	(28 + 37 + 32) ÷ 3 = 32.3	37 – 28 = 9
B	47	51	60	(47 + 51 + 60) ÷ 3 = 52.7	60 – 47 = 13
C	68	72	70	(68 + 72 + 70) ÷ 3 = 70.0	72 – 68 = 4

If the Data Comes in Categories, Present It in a Bar Chart

1) If either the independent or dependent variable is categoric (comes in distinct categories, e.g. blood types, metals) you should use a bar chart to display the data.

2) You also use them if one of the variables is discrete (the data can be counted in chunks, where there's no in-between value, e.g. number of people is discrete because you can't have half a person).

3) There are some golden rules you need to follow for drawing bar charts:

1 Remember to include the units.

2 Label both axes.

Ice Cream Sales in Froggartland and Broccoliland

Number sold (thousands)

Chocolate   Mint   Strawberry   Broccoli
Ice cream flavour

☐ Froggartland
☐ Broccoliland

5 If you've got more than one set of data include a key.

4 Draw it nice and big (covering at least half the graph paper).

3 Leave a gap between different categories.

Discrete variables love bar charts — although they'd never tell anyone that...

The stuff on this page might all seem a bit basic, but it's easy marks in the exams (which you'll kick yourself if you don't get). Examiners are a bit picky when it comes to bar charts — if you don't draw them properly they won't be happy. Also, double check any mean or range calculations you do, just to be sure they're correct.

Presenting Data

Scientists just <u>love</u> presenting data as <u>line graphs</u> (weirdos)...

If the Data is <u>Continuous</u>, Plot a <u>Line Graph</u>

1) If the independent and the dependent variable are <u>continuous</u> (numerical data that can have any value within a range, e.g. length, volume, temperature) you should use a <u>line graph</u> to display the data.

2) Here are the <u>rules</u> for <u>drawing</u> line graphs:

① Remember to include the <u>units</u>.

② Put the <u>dependent</u> variable (the thing you measure) on the <u>y-axis</u> (the <u>vertical</u> one).

③ <u>Label both axes</u>.

④ If you've got more than one set of data <u>include a key</u>.

⑤ Draw it nice and <u>big</u> (covering at least half the graph paper).

⑥ Put the <u>independent</u> variable (the thing you change) on the <u>x-axis</u> (the <u>horizontal</u> one).

Compression of a Spring with Different Loads

(graph: Compression (mm) vs Load (kg), with anomalous result marked)

⑧ To plot the points, use a <u>sharp pencil</u> and make a <u>neat little cross</u> (don't do blobs).

nice clear mark — smudged / unclear marks

⑦ <u>Don't join the dots up</u>. You need to draw a <u>line of best fit</u> (or a <u>curve of best fit</u> if your points make a curve).

When drawing a line (or curve), try to draw the line <u>through</u> or as <u>near</u> to <u>as many points as possible</u>, ignoring anomalous results.

3) Line graphs are used to <u>show the relationship</u> between two variables (just like other graphs).

4) Data can show <u>three</u> different types of correlation (relationship):

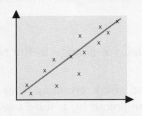

<u>POSITIVE</u> <u>correlation</u> — as one variable <u>increases</u> the other <u>increases</u>.

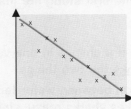

<u>NEGATIVE</u> <u>correlation</u> — as one variable <u>increases</u> the other <u>decreases</u>.

<u>NO correlation</u> — there's <u>no relationship</u> between the two variables.

5) You need to be able to describe the following relationships on line graphs too:

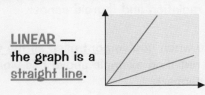

<u>LINEAR</u> — the graph is a <u>straight line</u>.

<u>DIRECTLY PROPORTIONAL</u> — both variables increase (or decrease) in the <u>same ratio</u>. The graph is a <u>straight line</u> which goes through the <u>origin</u> (0, 0).

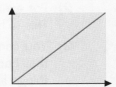

There's a positive correlation between revision and boredom...

...but there's also a positive correlation between <u>revision</u> and getting a <u>better mark in an exam</u>. Cover the page and write down the <u>eight things</u> you need to remember when <u>drawing line graphs</u>. No sneaky peeking either — I saw you.

Drawing Conclusions

Congratulations — you've made it to the fun part — drawing conclusions.

You Can Only Conclude What the Data Shows and NO MORE

1) Drawing conclusions might seem pretty straightforward — you just look at the data and say what pattern or relationship you see between the dependent and independent variables.

EXAMPLE: The table on the right shows the decrease in temperature of a beaker of hot water insulated with different materials over 10 minutes.

Material	Mean temperature decrease (°C)
A	4
B	2
No insulation	20

CONCLUSION: Material B reduces heat loss from the beaker more over a 10 minute period than material A.

2) But you've got to be really careful that your conclusion matches the data you've got and doesn't go any further.

3) You also need to be able to use the results to justify your conclusion (i.e. back up your conclusion with some specific data).

EXAMPLE continued: You can't conclude that material B would reduce heat loss by the same amount for any other type of container — the results could be totally different.

EXAMPLE continued: Material B reduced heat loss more than material A, since the temperature decrease was 2 °C less on average.

Correlation DOES NOT mean Cause

1) If two things are correlated (i.e. there's a relationship between them) it doesn't necessarily mean that a change in one variable is causing the change in the other — this is REALLY IMPORTANT, DON'T FORGET IT.

2) There are three possible reasons for a correlation:

① CHANCE

1) Even though it might seem a bit weird, it's possible that two things show a correlation in a study purely because of chance.

2) For example, one study might find a correlation between people's hair colour and how good they are at frisbee. But other scientists don't get a correlation when they investigate it — the results of the first study are just a fluke.

② LINKED BY A 3rd VARIABLE

1) A lot of the time it may look as if a change in one variable is causing a change in the other, but it isn't — a third variable links the two things.

2) For example, there's a correlation between water temperature and shark attacks. This obviously isn't because warmer water makes sharks crazy. Instead, they're linked by a third variable — the number of people swimming (more people swim when the water's hotter, and with more people in the water you get more shark attacks).

③ CAUSE

1) Sometimes a change in one variable does cause a change in the other.

2) For example, there's a correlation between exposure to radiation and thyroid cancer. This is because radiation can cause cancer.

3) You can only conclude that a correlation is due to cause when you've controlled all the variables that could, just could, be affecting the result. (For the radiation example above this would include things like age and exposure to other things that cause cancer).

I conclude that this page is a bit dull...

...yup, I lied at the start. Although, just because I find it dull doesn't mean that I can conclude it's dull (you might think it's the most interesting thing since that kid got his head stuck in the railings). In an exam you could be given a conclusion and asked whether the data supports it — so make sure you understand this page.

Planning and Evaluating Investigations

In an exam, you could be asked to plan or describe how you'd carry out an investigation. You might also be asked to say what you think of someone else's. Fear not, here's how you'd go about such things...

You Need to Be Able to Plan a Good Experiment

Here are some general tips on what to include when planning an experiment:

1) Say what you're measuring (i.e. what the dependent variable will be).
2) Say what you're changing (i.e. what the independent variable will be) and describe how you'll change it.
3) Describe the method and the apparatus you'd use (e.g. to measure the variables).
4) Describe what variables you're keeping constant — and how you're going to do it.
5) Say that you need to repeat the experiment three times, to make sure the results are repeatable.
6) Say whether you're using a control or not.

Here's an idea of the sort of thing you might be asked in an exam and what you might write as an answer...

Exam-style Question:

1   Describe an investigation to find how the type of surface under a wood block affects the force needed to slide the block across the surface.

Example Answer:

Attach a hook firmly to the centre of one of the faces of a wooden block so that a newton meter can be attached. Choose three different surfaces to place the block on. Use a spirit level to make sure they're all flat and horizontal.

Take a newton meter and calibrate it by suspending masses with a known weight from it and writing down the force shown. This will ensure its readings are accurate.

Place the wood block on the first surface, and hook the newton meter onto the block. Pull gently on the block using the newton meter in the horizontal direction until the block starts to move. Write down the force shown on the newton meter at this point. Repeat this experiment at least three times and calculate an average reading, discounting any anomalous results.

Do the same again for each type of surface. Between testing each surface, suspend one of the weights used for the initial calibration from the newton meter and check the reading is still the same. This will show whether the newton meter is still giving accurate readings.

You Could Be Asked to Evaluate An Investigation

And finally — you might be asked to evaluate (assess) someone's investigation, data or conclusion. You need to think about the following things:

1) Method: Was it a fair test? Was the best method of data collection used?
2) Repeatability: Were enough repeat measurements taken? Were the repeated measurements similar?
3) Reproducibility: Are the results comparable to similar experiments done by other people?
4) Validity: Does the data answer the original question?

If the answer to all of these questions is a firm 'yes', you can have a good degree of confidence in the data and conclusion. If the answer to any of them is 'no' or 'umm, I don't know', then you might want to reconsider the data and conclusion. Have a think about how the investigation could be improved to get repeatable, reproducible and valid results.

Plan your way to exam success...

You might have to write a long, extended answer to any questions like this in an exam. Just remember to think about what you're going to say beforehand and in what order — that way you're less likely to forget something important. Like what it is you're actually measuring, or what the different variables are, say.

Speed and Velocity

When you're talking about speed or forces, it's often not enough to just talk about the <u>magnitude</u> (<u>size</u>). You sometimes need to include a nod to <u>direction</u> too.

Vectors __Have__ __Size__ and __Direction__ — Scalar __Quantities Only Have Size__

1) Speed and velocity are both measured in m/s (or km/h or mph). They both say how fast you're going, but there's a subtle difference between them which you need to know.

2) To measure the <u>speed</u> of an object, you only need to measure <u>how fast</u> it's going — the <u>direction</u> is <u>not important</u>. E.g. speed = 30 mph.

3) <u>Velocity</u> is a <u>more useful</u> measure of <u>motion</u>, because it describes both the <u>speed and direction</u>. E.g. velocity = 30 mph due north.

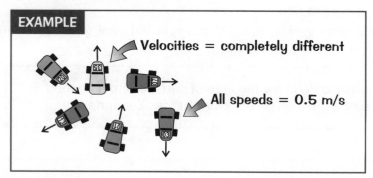

EXAMPLE

Velocities = completely different

All speeds = 0.5 m/s

4) A quantity like <u>speed</u>, that has only <u>magnitude</u> (size), is called a <u>scalar</u> quantity.

<u>Scalar quantities</u>:
speed, time, distance, temperature, mass, length, energy, etc.

5) A quantity like <u>velocity</u>, that has <u>magnitude</u> and <u>direction as well</u>, is a <u>vector</u> quantity.

<u>Vector quantities</u>:
velocity, force, displacement, acceleration, momentum, weight, etc.

Velocity, Displacement and Time — the __Formula:__

<u>Velocity</u> is just <u>speed in a given direction</u>.
So the <u>formula</u> for finding it is pretty much the same as for speed:

$$\text{Velocity} = \frac{\text{Displacement}}{\text{Time taken}}$$

If you're not sure how to use formula triangles, have a look inside the front cover.

Be careful, the s = displacement (distance in a given direction).

You really ought to get <u>pretty slick</u> with this <u>very easy formula</u>.
The <u>formula triangle</u> version makes it all a bit of a <u>breeze</u>.
You just need to try and think up some interesting word for remembering the <u>order</u> of the <u>letters</u> in the triangle, $v^s t$. Errm... verst, perhaps... well, you think up your own.

<u>Example</u>: A cat skulks 20 m due east in 35 s. Find: a) its velocity, b) how long it takes to skulk 75 m east.

<u>Answer</u>: Using the formula triangle: a) v = s/t = 20/35 = <u>0.57 m/s</u> (to 2 d.p.) due east.
b) t = s/v = 75/0.57 = 131 s = <u>2 min 11 s</u>

A lot of the time we tend to use the words "speed" and "velocity" interchangeably.
So to calculate speed you'd just use the above formula with distance instead of displacement.

Ah, velocity equals displacement over time — that old chestnut...

<u>Speed cameras</u> measure the speed of motorists using two photos taken a fraction of a second apart. The photos are then used to work out <u>how fast</u> the vehicle was going. And the photos always have the vehicle's number plate in them, so that's how they know who to put on the naughty step. Clever, eh?

Distance-Time Graphs

Ah, time for some graphs. Maths again so early on, what a delight...

Distance-Time Graphs

If an object is moving in a straight line, you can show how far
away from a certain point it is using a distance-time graph:

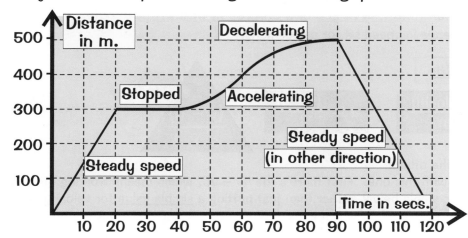

As you probably know,
speed = distance ÷ time.
So the gradient of a
distance-time graph tells
you how fast your object is
travelling. This is because
the gradient is the change in
the distance (vertical axis)
divided by the change in time
(horizontal axis). See — it's
easy when you know how.

Curves =
difficulty getting
out of chairs.

Very Important Notes:

1) Gradient = speed.
2) Flat sections are where it's stationary — it's stopped.
3) Straight uphill or downhill sections mean it is travelling at a steady speed.
4) The steeper the graph, the faster it's going.
5) Downhill sections mean it's going back toward its starting point.
6) Curves represent acceleration or deceleration.
7) A steepening curve means it's speeding up (increasing gradient).
8) A levelling off curve means it's slowing down (decreasing gradient).

Calculating Speed from a Distance-Time Graph — It's Just the Gradient

E.g the speed during the return section of the graph (from 90 s) is:

$$\text{Speed} = \text{gradient} = \frac{\text{vertical}}{\text{horizontal}} = \frac{500}{30} = \underline{16.7 \text{ m/s}}$$

Don't forget that you have to use
the scales of the axes to work out
the gradient. Don't measure in cm!

Calculating Speed from a Curved Region — It's Just the Gradient of a Tangent

The curved regions of a distance-time graph show the object
accelerating or decelerating. You can find the speed the object's
travelling at by finding the gradient of a tangent drawn at the
point you're interested in. A tangent is a straight line drawn just
touching the curve at that point. The tangent should form a right
angle with a normal drawn at that point.

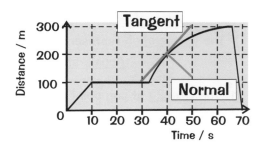

$$\text{Speed (at 40 s)} = \text{gradient} = \frac{\text{vertical}}{\text{horizontal}} = \frac{200}{20} = \underline{10 \text{ m/s}}$$

Don't speed through this page — learn it properly...

Distance-time graphs have an annoying habit of popping up in exams — so make sure you're confident with
drawing and interpreting them. Remember that the gradient of a distance-time graph is the speed — so the
steeper the line, the faster you're going. See — I told you it's simple when you know how.

Acceleration and Velocity-Time Graphs

I bet you loved that distance-time graph, huh? Well coming up soon is its big brother, the <u>velocity-time</u> graph.

Acceleration *is* How Quickly Velocity *is* Changing

Acceleration is <u>definitely not</u> the same as <u>velocity</u> or <u>speed</u>.

1) Acceleration is <u>how quickly</u> the velocity is <u>changing</u>.

2) This change in velocity can be a <u>CHANGE IN SPEED</u> or a <u>CHANGE IN DIRECTION</u> or <u>both</u>.

(You only have to worry about the change in speed bit for calculations.)

Acceleration — The Formula;

$$\text{Acceleration} = \frac{\text{Change in Velocity}}{\text{Time taken}}$$

$$a = \frac{(v - u)}{t}$$

$$\frac{(v - u)}{a \times t}$$

Here 'v' is the <u>final velocity</u> and 'u' is the <u>initial velocity</u>.

Well, it's <u>just another formula</u>.
And it's got a <u>formula triangle</u> like all the others.
Mind you, there are <u>two tricky things</u> with this one. First there's the '(v − u)', which means working out the '<u>change in velocity</u>', as shown in the example below, rather than just putting a <u>simple value</u> for velocity or speed in. Secondly there's the <u>unit</u> of acceleration, which is <u>m/s²</u>.
<u>Not m/s</u>, which is <u>velocity</u>, but <u>m/s²</u>. Got it? No? Let's try once more: <u>Not m/s</u>, but <u>m/s²</u>.

Acceleration is the change in velocity (m/s) per second (s), = m/s².

EXAMPLE: A skulking cat accelerates from 2 m/s to 6 m/s in 5.6 s. Find its acceleration.

ANSWER: Using the formula triangle: a = (v − u) / t = (6 − 2) / 5.6
= 4 / 5.6 = <u>0.71 m/s²</u>

Velocity-Time Graphs

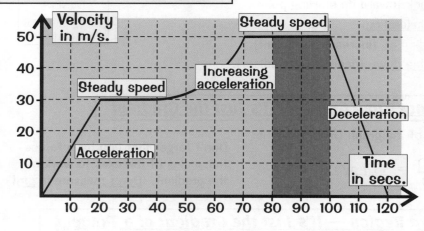

Very Important Notes:

1) <u>GRADIENT = ACCELERATION</u>.

2) <u>Flat sections</u> represent <u>steady speed</u>.

3) The <u>steeper</u> the graph, the <u>greater</u> the <u>acceleration</u> or <u>deceleration</u>.

4) <u>Uphill</u> sections (/) are <u>acceleration</u>.

5) <u>Downhill</u> sections (\) are <u>deceleration</u>.

6) The <u>area</u> under any section of the graph (or all of it) is equal to the <u>distance travelled</u> in that <u>time interval</u>.

7) A <u>curve</u> means <u>changing acceleration</u>.

Calculating Acceleration, Velocity and Distance from a Velocity-Time Graph

1) The <u>acceleration</u> represented by the <u>first section</u> of the graph is:

$$\underline{\text{Acceleration}} = \underline{\text{gradient}} = \frac{\text{vertical change}}{\text{horizontal change}} = \frac{30}{20} = \underline{1.5 \text{ m/s}^2}$$

2) The <u>velocity</u> at any point is simply found by <u>reading the value</u> off the <u>velocity axis</u>.

3) The <u>distance travelled</u> in any time interval is equal to the <u>area</u> under the graph. For example, the distance travelled between t = 80 s and t = 100 s is equal to the <u>shaded area</u>, which is equal to 20 × 50 = <u>1000 m</u>.

Understanding motion graphs — it can be a real uphill struggle...

Make sure you know all there is to know about velocity-time graphs — i.e. <u>learn those numbered points</u>.
You work out acceleration from the graph simply by applying the acceleration formula — change in velocity is the change on the vertical axis and time taken is the change on the horizontal axis.

Resultant Forces

A <u>force</u> is simply a <u>push</u> or a <u>pull</u>. There are really only <u>six different forces</u> that might pop up:

> 1) <u>GRAVITY</u> or <u>WEIGHT</u> (see page 23) always acting <u>straight downwards</u>.
> 2) <u>REACTION FORCE</u> from a <u>surface</u>, usually acting <u>straight upwards</u>.
> 3) <u>THRUST</u> or <u>PUSH</u> or <u>PULL</u> due to an engine or rocket <u>speeding something up</u>.
> 4) <u>DRAG</u> or <u>AIR RESISTANCE</u> or <u>FRICTION</u> which is <u>slowing the thing down</u>.
> 5) <u>LIFT</u> due to an <u>aeroplane wing</u>.
> 6) <u>TENSION</u> in a <u>rope</u> or <u>cable</u>.

Resultant Force _is the_ Overall Force _on a Point or Object_

The notion of <u>resultant force</u> is a really important one for you to get your head round:

1) In most <u>real</u> situations there are at least <u>two forces</u> acting on an object along any direction.

2) The <u>overall</u> effect of these forces will decide the <u>motion</u> of the object — whether it will <u>accelerate</u>, <u>decelerate</u> or stay at a <u>steady speed</u>.

3) If you have a <u>number of forces</u> acting at a single point, you can replace them with a <u>single force</u> (so long as the single force has the <u>same effect on the motion</u> as the original forces acting all together).

4) The overall force you get is called the <u>resultant force</u>.

5) If the forces all act along the same line (they're all parallel and act in the same or the opposite direction), the <u>resultant force</u> is found by just <u>adding</u> all the forces in one direction and <u>subtracting</u> all the forces in the opposite direction. If they're not along the same line it gets a bit harder (see next page).

Example: _Stationary Teapot — All Forces_ Balance

1) The force of <u>GRAVITY</u> (or weight) is acting <u>downwards</u>.

2) This causes a <u>REACTION FORCE</u> (see p. 18) from the surface <u>pushing up</u> on the object.

3) This is the <u>only way</u> it can be in <u>BALANCE</u>.

4) <u>Without</u> a reaction force, it would <u>accelerate downwards</u> due to the pull of gravity.

5) The <u>resultant</u> force on the teapot is zero: 10 N – 10 N = 0 N.

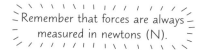

Remember that forces are always measured in newtons (N).

Example: _Steady Speed — All Forces in_ Balance!

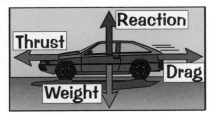

Thrust balances <u>drag</u>
Reaction balances <u>weight</u>

Drag balances <u>weight</u>

This skydiver is free-falling at 'terminal speed' (see p. 21).

A Resultant Force _Means a_ Change in Velocity

1) If there is a resultant force acting on an object, then the object will <u>change its state of rest or motion</u>.

2) In other words, it causes a <u>change in the object's velocity</u>. Exactly how is covered in more detail on page 17.

And you're moving forward — what a result...

Resultant forces really aren't that hard — the trick is to make sure you've <u>accounted for everything</u>.
Handily, there's more on <u>calculating</u> resultant forces coming up next, so don't panic. Phew...

Combining Forces

You might be asked to <u>calculate</u> the resultant force (or vector) from a diagram or some information. This means more maths I'm afraid. Sorry, but don't blame me, I didn't write the specification...

To Work Out Resultant Force — You Need To Combine Vectors

You can find the <u>resultant force</u> or forces acting along the <u>same line</u> by adding them <u>end to end</u>.

EXAMPLE: What's the resultant force of a 220 N force north, a 180 N force south and a 90 N force south?

Start by choosing a direction as the positive — let's say north. This means you <u>add</u> any forces in the north direction and <u>subtract</u> any forces in the south direction.

Resultant force = 220 – 180 – 90 = –50 N, so <u>50 N south</u>.

EXAMPLE: The jets on the plane are producing a thrust of 22 000 N east, and the friction from the air is 8000 N west at this speed. What is the resultant force acting on the plane?

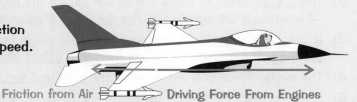

Friction from Air ⟵ ⟶ Driving Force From Engines

Let's say east is positive. You <u>add</u> any forces in the east direction and <u>subtract</u> any forces in the west direction.

Resultant force = 22 000 – 8000 = <u>14 000 N east</u>.

For Coplanar Forces NOT in a Straight Line Use Scale Drawings

The maths gets a bit trickier if the two forces are still in the same plane (they're <u>coplanar</u>) but they <u>aren't</u> <u>acting along the same line</u>. In a case like this, you need to do a <u>scale drawing</u> to work out the resultant force. Draw the forces, at the right scale, '<u>tip-to-tail</u>' then measure the <u>length</u> of the <u>resultant force</u> on the diagram (and the <u>angle</u> if needed). This is the <u>line</u> drawn from the <u>start</u> of the <u>first force</u> to the <u>end</u> of the <u>last force</u>.

EXAMPLE: A man is on an electric bicycle that pushes him with a force of 4 N north. However, the wind is pushing him with a force of 3 N east. Find the magnitude of the resultant force.

Start by drawing a scale diagram to illustrate the forces acting on the man. Make sure you choose a <u>sensible scale</u> (e.g. 1 cm = 1 N).

Then just <u>measure</u> the missing side with a ruler.

It's = <u>5 cm</u> long, so the resultant force is <u>5 N</u>.

(If you were asked to find <u>direction</u> as well, you would just measure the <u>angle</u> θ with a protractor.)

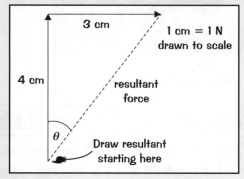

What's a vector's favourite band? One Direction...

You use the same trick to combine <u>other vectors</u> — velocity, momentum, displacement, acceleration, anything. Just draw the vectors end to end and, with a bit of simple maths, you can find the overall (resultant) vector.

Section One — Forces and Their Effects

Forces and Acceleration

Around about the time of the Great Plague in the 1660s, a chap called <u>Isaac Newton</u> worked out his <u>Laws of Motion</u>. At first they might seem kind of obscure or irrelevant, but to be perfectly blunt, if you can't understand this page then you'll never understand <u>forces and motion</u>.

An Object Needs a Force to Start Moving

> If the resultant force on a <u>stationary</u> object is <u>zero</u>, the object will <u>remain stationary</u>.

Things <u>don't just start moving</u> on their own, there has to be a <u>resultant force</u> (see p. 15) to get them started.

No Resultant Force Means No Change in Velocity

> If there is <u>no resultant force</u> on a <u>moving</u> object it'll just carry on moving at the <u>same velocity</u> (at the <u>same speed</u> and in the <u>same direction</u>).

1) When a train or car or bus or anything else is <u>moving</u> at a <u>constant velocity</u> then the <u>forces</u> on it must all be <u>balanced</u>.

2) Never let yourself entertain the <u>ridiculous idea</u> that things need a constant overall force to <u>keep</u> them moving — NO NO NO NO NO NO!

3) To keep going at a <u>steady speed</u>, there must be <u>zero resultant force</u> — and don't you forget it.

A Resultant Force Means Acceleration

> If there is a <u>non-zero resultant force</u>, then the object will <u>accelerate</u> in the direction of the force.

1) A non-zero <u>resultant</u> force will always produce <u>acceleration</u> (or deceleration).

2) This "<u>acceleration</u>" can take <u>five</u> different forms: <u>Starting</u>, <u>stopping</u>, <u>speeding up</u>, <u>slowing down</u> and <u>changing direction</u>.

3) On a force diagram, the <u>arrows</u> will be <u>unequal</u>:

<u>Don't ever say</u>: "If something's moving there must be an overall resultant force acting on it".
Not so. If there's an <u>overall</u> force it will always <u>accelerate</u>.
You get <u>steady</u> speed when there is <u>zero</u> resultant force.
I wonder how many times I need to say that same thing before you remember it?

Steady Speed Bus Tours Ltd. — providing consistent service since 1926...

<u>Objects in space</u> don't need a driving force to keep travelling at a steady speed — it's only because of <u>air resistance</u> and <u>friction</u> that we do. A steady speed means that there is <u>zero resultant force</u>.

Forces and Acceleration

More fun stuff on forces and acceleration here. The big equation to learn is <u>F = ma</u> — it's a really important one and you <u>will</u> be tested on it. Remember that the F is always the <u>resultant force</u> — that's important too.

A <u>Non-Zero</u> Resultant Force Produces an Acceleration

Any <u>resultant force</u> will produce <u>acceleration</u>, and this is the <u>formula</u> for it:

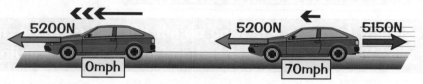

$$F = ma \quad \text{or} \quad a = F/m$$

m = mass in kilograms (kg)
a = acceleration in metres per second squared (m/s²)
F is the <u>resultant force</u> in newtons (N)

<u>EXAMPLE</u>: A car of mass of 1750 kg has an engine which provides a driving force of 5200 N.
At 70 mph the drag force acting on the car is 5150 N.
Find its acceleration a) when first setting off from rest b) at 70 mph.

<u>ANSWER</u>: 1) First draw a force diagram for both cases (no need to show the vertical forces):

5200N 0mph | 5200N 5150N 70mph

2) Work out the resultant force and acceleration of the car in each case.

Resultant force = 5200 N
a = F/m = 5200 ÷ 1750 = <u>3.0 m/s²</u>

Resultant force = 5200 – 5150 = 50 N
a = F/m = 50 ÷ 1750 = <u>0.03 m/s²</u>

Reaction Forces <u>are</u> Equal <u>and</u> Opposite

When <u>two objects interact</u>, the forces they exert on each other are <u>equal and opposite</u>.

1) That means if you <u>push</u> something, say a shopping trolley, the trolley will <u>push back</u> against you, <u>just as hard</u>.

2) And as soon as you <u>stop</u> pushing, <u>so does the trolley</u>. Kinda clever really.

3) So far so good. The slightly tricky thing to get your head round is this — if the forces are always equal, <u>how does anything ever go anywhere</u>? The important thing to remember is that the two forces are acting on <u>different objects</u>. Think about a pair of ice skaters:

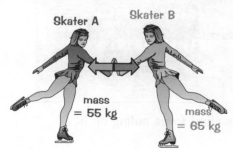

Skater A Skater B
mass = 55 kg mass = 65 kg

When skater A pushes on skater B (the '<u>action</u>' force), she feels an equal and opposite force from skater B's hand (the '<u>reaction</u>' force). Both skaters feel the <u>same sized force</u>, in <u>opposite directions</u>, and so accelerate away from each other.

Skater A will be <u>accelerated</u> more than skater B, though, because she has a smaller mass — remember <u>a = F/m</u>.

4) It's the same sort of thing when you go <u>swimming</u>. You <u>push</u> back against the <u>water</u> with your arms and legs, and the water pushes you forwards with an <u>equal-sized force</u> in the <u>opposite direction</u>.

I have a reaction to forces — they bring me out in a rash...

This is the real deal. Like... proper Physics. It was <u>pretty fantastic</u> at the time it was discovered — suddenly people understood how forces and motion worked, they could work out the <u>orbits of planets</u> and everything. Inspired? No? Shame. Learn it anyway — you're really going to struggle in the exam if you don't.

Momentum and Collisions

A <u>large</u> rhino running very <u>fast</u> at you is going to be a lot harder to stop than a scrawny one out for a Sunday afternoon stroll — that's momentum for you.

Momentum = Mass × Velocity

1) Momentum (p) is a <u>property</u> of <u>moving objects</u>.
2) The <u>greater</u> the <u>mass</u> of an object and the <u>greater</u> its <u>velocity</u> (see p. 12) the <u>more momentum</u> the object has.
3) Momentum is a <u>vector</u> quantity — it has size <u>and</u> direction (like <u>velocity</u>, but not speed).

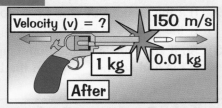

Momentum (kg m/s) = Mass (kg) × Velocity (m/s)

Momentum *Before* = Momentum *After*

In a <u>closed system</u>, the total momentum <u>before</u> an event (e.g. a collision) is the same as <u>after</u> the event. This is called <u>Conservation of Momentum</u>.

> A <u>closed system</u> is just a fancy way of saying that no external forces act.

Example 1: Collisions

Two skaters approach each other, collide and move off together as shown. At what velocity do they move after the collision?

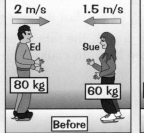

1) Choose which direction is <u>positive</u>.
   I'll say "<u>positive</u>" means "<u>to the right</u>".
2) <u>Total momentum before</u> collision
   = momentum of Ed + momentum of Sue
   = {80 × 2} + {60 × (–1.5)}
   = <u>70 kg m/s</u>
3) <u>Total momentum after</u> collision
   = momentum of Ed and Sue together
   = <u>140 × v</u>
4) So 140v = 70, i.e. <u>v = 0.5 m/s to the right</u>

Example 2: Explosions

A gun fires a bullet as shown. At what speed does the gun move backwards?

1) Choose which direction is <u>positive</u>. Again, I reckon "<u>positive</u>" means "<u>to the right</u>".
2) <u>Total momentum before</u> firing = <u>0 kg m/s</u>
3) <u>Total momentum after</u> firing
   = momentum of bullet + momentum of gun
   = (0.01 × 150) + (1 × v)
   = <u>1.5 + v</u>

> This is the gun's recoil.

The momentum of a system <u>before</u> an explosion is <u>zero</u>, so, due to <u>conservation of momentum</u>, the total momentum after an explosion is <u>zero too</u>.

4) So 1.5 + v = 0, i.e. v = –1.5 m/s
   So the gun moves <u>backwards</u> at <u>1.5 m/s</u>.

Forces *Cause* Changes *in* Momentum

1) When a <u>force</u> acts on an object, it causes a <u>change</u> in momentum.
2) A <u>larger</u> force means a <u>faster</u> change of momentum (and so a greater <u>acceleration</u>).
3) Likewise, if someone's momentum changes <u>very quickly</u> (like in a <u>car crash</u>), the <u>forces</u> on the body will be very <u>large</u>, and more likely to cause <u>injury</u>.
4) This is why cars are designed with safety features that slow people down over a <u>longer time</u> when they have a crash — the longer it takes for a change in <u>momentum</u>, the <u>smaller</u> the <u>force</u>. You need to know a bit more detail than this though, so there's more on the next page...

Learn this stuff — it'll only take a moment... um...

Momentum's a pretty fundamental bit of Physics — so make sure you learn it properly. Right then, momentum is always <u>conserved</u> in collisions and explosions when there are no external forces acting. Job's a good 'un.

Momentum and Safety

As briefly explained earlier, the Physics of momentum can be applied to the real world to design <u>safe</u> cars and other things. It's all about forces and the rate of change of momentum. <u>Sweet as a nut</u>.

Forces **Cause** Changes **in** Momentum

1) When a <u>force</u> acts on an object, it causes a <u>change in momentum</u>.

$$\text{Force acting (N)} = \frac{\text{Change in momentum (kg m/s)}}{\text{Time taken for change to happen (s)}}$$

$$\frac{\Delta p}{F \times t}$$

<u>EXAMPLE</u>: A rock with mass <u>1 kg</u> is travelling through space at <u>15 m/s</u>.
A comet hits the rock, giving it a resultant force of <u>2500 N</u> for <u>0.7 seconds</u>.
Calculate a) the rock's <u>initial momentum</u>,
and b) the <u>change</u> in its momentum resulting from the impact.

<u>ANSWER</u>: a) Momentum = mass × velocity = 1 × 15 = <u>15 kg m/s</u>
b) Using the <u>formula triangle</u>,
Change of momentum = force × time = 2500 × 0.7 = <u>1750 kg m/s</u>.

2) It's the amount of <u>time taken</u> for a change in momentum that determines how big or small the force is. If the change in momentum stays the same and <u>t is small</u>, <u>F will be big</u>, but if <u>t is big</u>, <u>F will be small</u>.

3) So if someone's momentum changes <u>very quickly</u> (like in a <u>car crash</u>), the rate of change of momentum is big and so the <u>forces</u> on the body will be very <u>large</u>, and more likely to cause <u>injury</u>.

Safety Features **Reduce Forces**

1) If your momentum changes <u>slowly</u>, like in nice controlled braking in a car, the <u>forces</u> acting on your body are <u>small</u> and you're unlikely to be <u>hurt</u>.

2) In a <u>collision</u>, you <u>can't really affect</u> the <u>change in momentum</u> — whatever you do, the car's <u>mass</u> and its <u>change in velocity</u> stay <u>the same</u>. However, the average <u>force</u> on an object can be <u>lowered</u> by <u>slowing the object down</u> over a <u>longer time</u>.

3) <u>Safety features</u> in a car <u>increase the collision time</u>. This <u>decreases the rate of change of momentum</u> and so <u>reduces the forces</u> on the passengers:

<u>SEAT BELTS</u> stretch slightly, <u>increasing the time</u> taken for the wearer to stop. This <u>decreases the rate of change of momentum</u> and so <u>reduces the forces</u> acting on the chest.

<u>AIR BAGS</u> also slow you down more <u>gradually</u>.

4) These ideas are also used for <u>safety features</u> that aren't found in cars:

<u>CYCLE AND MOTORCYCLE HELMETS</u> provide padding that <u>increases the time</u> taken for your head to come to a stop if it <u>hits something hard</u>.

<u>CUSHIONED SURFACES IN PLAYGROUNDS</u>
Yup, you've guessed it. They <u>increase the time</u> of the fall, decreasing the rate of change of momentum and so reducing the forces acting, so children are <u>less likely to be hurt</u>.

<u>CRASH MATS IN GYMS</u> increase the <u>length of time</u> of impact, and so <u>reduce the forces</u> acting on you.

<u>Don't let all this revising drive you crazy...</u>

Driving can be quite <u>risky</u> when you look at the Physics of it — which is why so much time and effort is put into making cars as safe as possible. This page isn't too bad really, so get it learnt. Pronto.

Frictional Force and Terminal Velocity

Ever wondered why it's so hard to run into a hurricane whilst wearing a sandwich board? Read on to find out...

Friction *is Always There to Slow Things Down*

1) If an object has <u>no force</u> propelling it along it will always <u>slow down and stop</u> because of <u>friction</u> (unless you're in space where there's nothing to rub against).

2) Friction always acts in the <u>opposite</u> direction to movement.

3) To travel at a <u>steady</u> speed, the driving force needs to <u>balance</u> the frictional forces.

4) You get friction between <u>two surfaces</u> in contact, or when an object passes <u>through a fluid</u> (<u>drag</u>).

RESISTANCE OR "DRAG" FROM FLUIDS (air or liquid)

Most of the resistive forces are caused by <u>air resistance</u> or "<u>drag</u>".
The most important factor <u>by far</u> in <u>reducing drag</u> in fluids is keeping the shape of the object <u>streamlined</u>.
The <u>opposite</u> extreme is a <u>parachute</u> which is about as <u>high drag</u> as you can get — which is, of course, <u>the whole idea</u>.

Drag *Increases* as the *Speed Increases*

<u>Frictional forces</u> from fluids always <u>increase with speed</u>.
A car has <u>much more</u> friction to <u>work against</u> when travelling at <u>70 mph</u> compared to <u>30 mph</u>. So at 70 mph the engine has to work <u>much harder</u> just to maintain a <u>steady speed</u>.

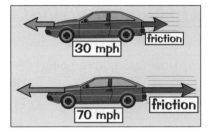

Objects *Falling Through* Fluids *Reach a* Terminal Velocity

When falling objects first <u>set off</u>, the force of gravity is <u>much more</u> than the <u>frictional force</u> slowing them down, so they accelerate. As the <u>speed increases</u> the friction <u>builds up</u>. This gradually <u>reduces</u> the <u>acceleration</u> until eventually the <u>frictional force</u> is <u>equal</u> to the <u>accelerating force</u> and then it won't accelerate any more. It will have reached its maximum speed or <u>terminal velocity</u> and will fall at a steady speed.

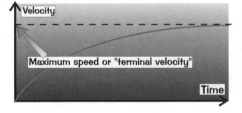

The Terminal Velocity *of* Falling Objects *Depends on their* Shape *and* Area

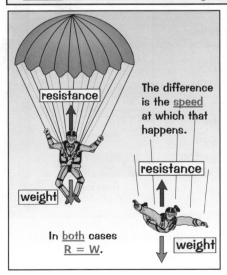

The difference is the <u>speed</u> at which that happens.

In <u>both</u> cases $R = W$.

The <u>accelerating force</u> acting on <u>all</u> falling objects is <u>gravity</u> and it would make them all fall at the <u>same</u> rate, if it wasn't for <u>air resistance</u>. This means that on the Moon, where there's <u>no air</u>, hamsters and feathers dropped simultaneously will hit the ground <u>together</u>. However, on Earth, <u>air resistance</u> causes things to fall at <u>different</u> speeds, and the <u>terminal velocity</u> of any object is determined by its <u>drag</u> in <u>comparison</u> to its <u>weight</u>.
The frictional force depends on its <u>shape and area</u>.

The most important example is the human <u>skydiver</u>. Without his parachute open he has quite a <u>small</u> area and a force of "<u>W = mg</u>" (see p. 23) pulling him down. He reaches a <u>terminal velocity</u> of about <u>120 mph</u>. But with the parachute <u>open</u>, there's much more <u>air resistance</u> (at any given speed) and still only the same force "<u>W = mg</u>" pulling him down. This means his <u>terminal velocity</u> comes right down to about <u>15 mph</u>, which is a <u>safe speed</u> to hit the ground at.

Learning about air resistance — it can be a real drag...

There are a few really important things on this page. 1) When you fall through a fluid, there's a frictional force (drag), 2) frictional force increases with speed, so 3) you eventually reach terminal velocity.

Stopping Distances

And now a page on stopping distances. This may seem a bit out of kilter with the rest of the section, but it's a <u>real world application</u> of the physics of forces. See, I told you it was useful... and fun... right?

Many Factors **Affect Your Total** Stopping Distance

1) Looking at things simply — if you <u>need to stop</u> in a <u>given distance</u>, then the <u>faster</u> a vehicle's going, the <u>bigger braking force</u> it'll need.

2) Likewise, for any given braking force, the <u>faster</u> you're going, the <u>greater your stopping distance</u>. But in real life it's not quite that simple — if your maximum braking force isn't enough, you'll go further before you stop.

3) The total <u>stopping distance</u> of a vehicle is the distance covered in the time between the driver <u>first spotting</u> a hazard and the vehicle coming to a <u>complete stop</u>.

4) The <u>stopping distance</u> is <u>the sum</u> of the <u>thinking distance</u> and the <u>braking distance</u>.

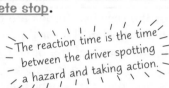

The reaction time is the time between the driver spotting a hazard and taking action.

1) Thinking Distance

"The distance the vehicle travels during the driver's reaction time".

It's affected by <u>two main factors</u>:

a) How fast you're going — Obviously. Whatever your reaction time, the <u>faster</u> you're going, the <u>further</u> you'll go.

b) How dopey you are — This is affected by <u>tiredness</u>, <u>drugs</u>, <u>alcohol</u> and a <u>careless</u> blasé attitude.

<u>Bad visibility</u> and <u>distractions</u> can also be a major factor in accidents — lashing rain, messing about with the radio, bright oncoming lights, etc. might mean that a driver <u>doesn't notice</u> a hazard until they're quite close to it. It <u>doesn't</u> affect your thinking distance, but you <u>start thinking</u> about stopping <u>nearer</u> to the hazard, and so you're <u>more likely</u> to crash.

The figures below for typical stopping distances are from the Highway Code. It's frightening to see just how far it takes to stop when you're going at 70 mph.

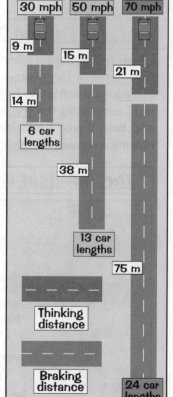

2) Braking Distance

"The distance the car travels under the braking force".

It's affected by <u>four main factors</u>:

a) How fast you're going — The <u>faster</u> you're going, the <u>further</u> it takes to stop.

b) How good your brakes are — All brakes must be checked and maintained <u>regularly</u>. Worn or faulty brakes will let you down <u>catastrophically</u> just when you need them the <u>most</u>, i.e. in an <u>emergency</u>.

c) How good the tyres are — Tyres should have a minimum <u>tread depth</u> of <u>1.6 mm</u> in order to be able to get rid of the <u>water</u> in wet conditions. Leaves, diesel spills and muck on the road can <u>greatly increase</u> the braking distance, and cause the car to <u>skid</u> too.

d) How good the grip is — This depends on <u>three things</u>:
1) <u>road surface</u>, 2) <u>weather</u> conditions, 3) <u>tyres</u>.

<u>Wet</u> or <u>icy roads</u> are always much more <u>slippy</u> than dry roads, but often you only discover this when you try to <u>brake</u> hard. You don't have as much grip, so you travel further before stopping.

Stop right there — and learn this page...

Without <u>tread</u>, a tyre will simply <u>ride</u> on a <u>layer of water</u> and skid <u>very easily</u>. This is called "<u>aquaplaning</u>" and isn't nearly as cool as it sounds. <u>Snow and ice</u> are also very hazardous because it is difficult for the tyres to <u>get a grip</u>.

Weight, Mass and Gravity

Now for something a bit more attractive — the force of gravity. Enjoy...

Gravitational Force is the Force of Attraction Between All Masses

Gravity attracts all masses, but you only notice it when one of the masses is really really big, e.g. a planet. Anything near a planet or star is attracted to it very strongly.

This has two important effects:

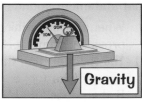

1) On the surface of a planet, it makes all things accelerate (see p. 14) towards the ground (all with the same acceleration, g, which is about 10 m/s^2 on Earth).

2) It gives everything a weight.

Weight and Mass are Not the Same

1) Mass is just the amount of 'stuff' in an object. For any given object this will have the same value anywhere in the universe.

2) Weight is caused by the pull of the gravitational force. In most questions the weight of an object is just the force of gravity pulling it towards the centre of the Earth.

3) An object has the same mass whether it's on Earth or on the Moon — but its weight will be different. A 1 kg mass will weigh less on the Moon (about 1.6 N) than it does on Earth (about 10 N), simply because the gravitational force pulling on it is less.

4) Weight is a force measured in newtons. It's measured using a spring balance or newton meter. Mass is not a force. It's measured in kilograms with a mass balance (an old-fashioned pair of balancing scales).

The Very Important Formula Relating Mass, Weight and Gravity

> weight = mass × gravitational field strength

$$W = m \times g$$

1) Remember, weight and mass are not the same. Mass is in kg, weight is in newtons.

2) The letter "g" represents the strength of gravity (which is also called gravitational field strength, acceleration due to gravity or acceleration of free fall) and its value is different for different planets. On Earth g ≈ 10 N/kg. On the Moon, where the gravity is weaker, g is only about 1.6 N/kg.

3) This formula is hideously easy to use:

Example: What is the weight, in newtons, of a 5 kg mass, both on Earth and on the Moon?
Answer: "W = m × g". On Earth: W = 5 × 10 = 50 N (The weight of the 5 kg mass is 50 N.)
On the Moon: W = 5 × 1.6 = 8 N (The weight of the 5 kg mass is 8 N.)

See what I mean. Hideously easy — as long as you've learnt what all the letters mean.

I don't think you understand the gravity of this situation...

The difference between weight and mass can be tricky to get your head around, but it's well important. Weight is the force of gravity acting on a mass, and mass is the amount of stuff, measured in kg. Now might be a good time to get that equation memorised as well — that's right — cover, scribble and check.

Work and Potential Energy

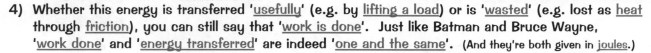

When a force moves an object through a distance, ENERGY IS TRANSFERRED and WORK IS DONE.

That statement sounds far more complicated than it needs to. Try this:

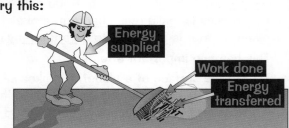

1) Whenever something moves, something else is providing some sort of 'effort' to move it.
2) The thing putting the effort in needs a supply of energy (like fuel or food or electricity etc.).
3) It then does 'work' by moving the object — and one way or another it transfers the energy it receives (as fuel) into other forms.
4) Whether this energy is transferred 'usefully' (e.g. by lifting a load) or is 'wasted' (e.g. lost as heat through friction), you can still say that 'work is done'. Just like Batman and Bruce Wayne, 'work done' and 'energy transferred' are indeed 'one and the same'. (And they're both given in joules.)

It's Just Another Trivial Formula:

Work Done = Force × Distance

$$\frac{W}{F \times d}$$

Whether the force is friction or weight or tension in a rope, it's always the same. To find how much energy has been transferred (in joules), you just multiply the force in N by the distance moved in m. Easy as that. I'll show you...

EXAMPLE: Some hooligan kids drag an old tractor tyre 5 m over rough ground. They pull with a total force of 340 N. Find the energy transferred.
ANSWER: W = F×d = 340 × 5 = 1700 J. Phew — easy peasy isn't it?

Gravitational Potential Energy is Energy Due to Height

Gravitational Potential Energy = mass × g × height

$$\frac{E_p}{m \times g \times h}$$

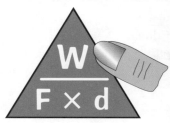

Potential energy at this height = m x g x h

No height above ground, so no potential energy

Gravitational potential energy (measured in joules) is the energy that an object has by virtue of (because of) its vertical position in a gravitational field. When an object is raised vertically, work is done against the force of gravity (it takes effort to lift it up) and the object gains gravitational potential energy. On Earth the gravitational field strength (g) is approximately 10 N/kg.

EXAMPLE: A sheep of mass 47 kg is slowly raised through 6.3 m. Find the gain in potential energy.
ANSWER: Just plug the numbers into the formula:
E_p = mgh = 47 × 10 × 6.3 = 2961 J
(Joules because it's energy.)

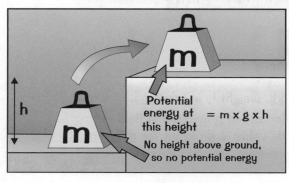

What do you call a sheep with no eyes and no legs?
Dunno?
A Cloud!

Revise work done — what else...

Remember "energy transferred" and "work done" are the same thing. By lifting something up you do work by transferring chemical energy to gravitational potential energy. Think about that next time you're bench-pressing sheep.

Kinetic Energy

Kinetic Energy is Energy of Movement

Anything that's moving has kinetic energy. Here's the formula:

$$\text{Kinetic Energy} = \tfrac{1}{2} \times \text{mass} \times \text{speed}^2$$

EXAMPLE: A car of mass 2450 kg is travelling at 38 m/s.
Calculate its kinetic energy.

ANSWER: It's pretty easy. You just plug the numbers into the formula — but watch the 'v²'!
$E_k = \tfrac{1}{2}mv^2 = \tfrac{1}{2} \times 2450 \times 38^2 = \underline{1\,768\,900 \text{ J}}$ (Joules because it's energy.)

1) Remember, the kinetic energy of something depends on both mass and speed.
The higher its mass and the faster it's going, the bigger its kinetic energy will be.

2) If you look at the formula you should be able to see that if mass doubles, the E_k doubles.

3) BUT if you double the speed, the E_k quadruples (increases by a factor of 4) — because of the 'v²'.

Kinetic Energy Transferred is Work Done

> Conservation of energy states that energy can never be created or destroyed — only converted into different forms.

When a Car is Moving It Has Kinetic Energy

1) A moving car can have a lot of kinetic energy. To slow a car down this kinetic energy needs
to be converted into other types of energy (using the law of conservation of energy).

2) To stop a car, the kinetic energy ($\tfrac{1}{2}mv^2$) has to be converted to heat energy as friction
between the wheels and the brake pads, causing the temperature of the brakes to increase:

$$\text{Kinetic Energy Transferred} = \text{Work Done by Brakes}$$
$$\tfrac{1}{2}mv^2 = F \times d$$

m = mass of car and passengers   v = speed of car   F = maximum braking force   d = braking distance
(in kg)   (in m/s)   (in N)   (in m).

3) Because 'F' is always the maximum possible braking force (which can't be increased), if you double
the speed, then d must increase by a factor of four to make the equation balance.

4) In other words, if you go twice as fast, the braking distance
must increase by a factor of four to convert the extra E_k.

Falling Objects Convert E_P into E_K...

When something falls, its potential energy (see p. 24) is converted
into kinetic energy. So the further it falls, the faster it goes.

$$\text{Kinetic energy gained} = \text{Potential Energy lost}$$

> This works the other way round too, e.g. if you run then jump into the air, your E_k becomes E_p.

...and some of this E_K is Transferred into Heat and Sound

1) When meteors and space shuttles enter the atmosphere, they have a very high kinetic energy.

2) Friction due to collisions with particles in the atmosphere transfers some of their kinetic energy to
heat energy and work is done.

3) The temperatures can become so extreme that most meteors burn up completely and never hit the Earth.
Only the biggest meteors make it through to the Earth's surface — these are called meteorites.

4) Space shuttles have heat shields made from special materials which lose heat quickly,
allowing the shuttle to re-enter the atmosphere without burning up.

Kinetic energy — just get a move on and learn it, OK...

So that's why I've not been hit by a meteor — most get burned up. Now I know. Fancy...

Forces and Elasticity

Forces aren't just important for cars and falling apples — you can <u>stretch things</u> with them as well. It can sound quite tricky at first, but it's not as hard as it looks. And there is only one equation to memorise — hurrah.

Work Done to an <u>Elastic Object</u> is <u>Stored</u> as <u>Elastic Potential Energy</u>

1) When you apply a force to an object you may cause it to <u>stretch</u> and <u>change in shape</u>.

2) Any object that can <u>go back</u> to its <u>original shape</u> after the force has been removed is an <u>elastic object</u> — it behaves <u>elastically</u>.

3) <u>Work is done</u> to an elastic object to <u>change</u> its shape. This energy is not lost but is <u>stored</u> by the object as <u>elastic potential energy</u>.

4) The elastic potential energy is then <u>converted to kinetic energy</u> when the <u>force is removed</u> and the object returns to its original shape, e.g. when a spring or an elastic band bounces back.

Elastic potential energy — useful for passing exams and scaring small children.

<u>Extension</u> of an Elastic Object is <u>Directly Proportional</u> to Force...

If a spring is supported at the top and then a weight attached to the bottom, it <u>stretches</u>.

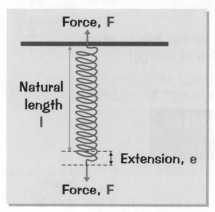

Force, F

Natural length l

Extension, e

Force, F

1) The <u>extension</u>, <u>e</u>, of a stretched spring (or other elastic object) is <u>directly proportional</u> to the load or <u>force</u> applied, <u>F</u>. The extension is measured in metres, and the force is measured in newtons.

2) This is the equation you need to learn: $$F = k \times e$$

3) k is the <u>spring constant</u>. Its value depends on the <u>material</u> that you are stretching and it's measured in newtons per metre (N/m).

...but this <u>Stops Working</u> when the <u>Force is Great Enough</u>

There's a <u>limit</u> to the amount of force you can apply to an object for the extension to keep on increasing <u>proportionally</u>.

1) The graph shows <u>force against extension</u> for an elastic object.

2) For small forces, force and extension are <u>proportional</u>. So the first part of the graph shows a straight-line relationship between force and extension.

3) There is a <u>maximum</u> force that the elastic object can take and still extend proportionally. This is known as the <u>limit of proportionality</u> and is shown on the graph at the point marked P.

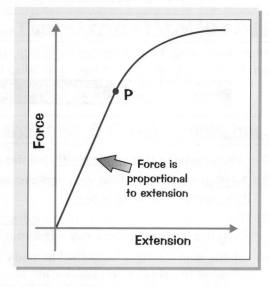

P

Force

Force is proportional to extension

Extension

I could make a joke, but I don't want to stretch myself...

Scaring small children aside, elastic potential is really <u>quite a useful</u> form of energy. Think of all the things we rely on that use it — catapults, trampolines, scrunchies... Ah, elastic potential energy — thank you for enriching our lives.

Power

Power is a concept that pops up in both <u>forces</u> and <u>electricity</u> (coming up later). This is because, at its most fundamental level, power is just about the rate of <u>energy transfer</u>.

Power *is the "Rate of Doing Work" — i.e. How Much per Second*

<u>Power</u> is <u>not</u> the same thing as <u>force</u>, nor <u>energy</u>. A <u>powerful</u> machine is not necessarily one which can exert a strong <u>force</u> (though it usually ends up that way).
A <u>powerful</u> machine is one which transfers <u>a lot of energy in a short space of time</u>.
This is the <u>very easy formula</u> for power:

$$\text{Power} = \frac{\text{Work done (or energy transferred)}}{\text{Time taken}}$$

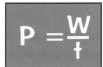

$$P = \frac{W}{t}$$

Power *is Measured in Watts (or J/s)*

The proper unit of power is the <u>watt</u>. <u>One watt = 1 joule of energy transferred per second</u>.
<u>Power</u> means "how much energy <u>per second</u>", so <u>watts</u> are the same as "<u>joules per second</u>" (J/s).
Don't ever say "watts per second" — it's <u>nonsense</u>.

<u>Example:</u>   A motor transfers 4.8 kJ of useful energy in 2 minutes. Find its power output.
<u>Answer:</u>   P = W / t = 4800/120 = 40 W (or 40 J/s)
(Note that the kJ had to be turned into J, and the minutes into seconds.)

4.8 kJ of useful
energy in <u>2 minutes</u>

Calculating Your Power Output

There are a few different ways to measure the power output of a <u>person</u>:

a) *The Timed Run Upstairs:*

In this case the "<u>energy transferred</u>" is the <u>potential energy you gain</u> (= mgh).
Hence <u>Power = mgh/t</u>

62 kg   12 m
Time taken
=14 s

Power output
= En. transferred/time
= mgh/t
= $(62 \times 10 \times 12) \div 14$
= <u>531 W</u>

b) *The Timed Acceleration:*

This time the <u>energy transferred</u> is the <u>kinetic energy you gain</u> (= ½mv²).
Hence <u>Power = ½mv²/t</u>

62 kg   0 ➡ 8 m/s
time taken = 4 s

Power output
= En. transferred/time
= ½mv²/t
= $(½ \times 62 \times 8^2) \div 4$
= <u>496 W</u>

To get <u>accurate results</u> from these experiments, you have to do them several times and find an <u>average</u>.

Power — you need to know watt's watt...

Power is the amount of energy transferred per second, and it's measured in <u>watts</u>. The watt is named after James Watt, a Scottish inventor and engineer who did a lot of work on steam engines in the 1700s. Nice. Make sure you <u>learn the formula</u> and power questions should be a doddle.

Turning Forces and the Centre of Mass

Moments, they're magic. Or maybe not. Either way, expect to be royally sick of pivots by the end of the page.

A Moment is the Turning Effect of a Force

The size of the moment of the force is given by:

MOMENT = FORCE × perpendicular DISTANCE from the line of action of the force to the pivot

Moment of the force in newton-metres (Nm). → $M = F \times d$ ← Distance in metres (m).
Force in newtons (N).

1) The force on the spanner causes a turning effect or moment on the nut (which acts as a pivot). A larger force would mean a larger moment.

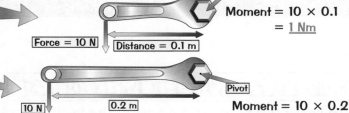

Tough nut
Force = 10 N   Distance = 0.1 m
Moment = 10 × 0.1
= 1 Nm

2) Using a longer spanner, the same force can exert a larger moment because the distance from the pivot is greater (see p. 29).

10 N   0.2 m   Pivot
Moment = 10 × 0.2
= 2 Nm

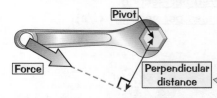

Pivot
Force
Perpendicular distance

3) To get the maximum moment (or turning effect) you need to push at right angles (perpendicular) to the spanner.

4) Pushing at any other angle means a smaller moment because the perpendicular distance between the line of action and the pivot is smaller.

The Centre of Mass Hangs Directly Below the Point of Suspension

1) You can think of the centre of mass of an object as the point at which the whole mass is concentrated.

2) A freely suspended object will swing until its centre of mass is vertically below the point of suspension.

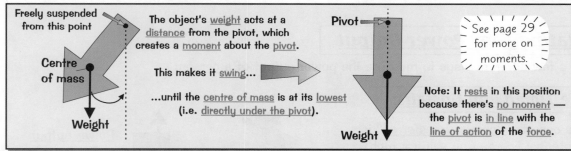

Freely suspended from this point

The object's weight acts at a distance from the pivot, which creates a moment about the pivot.

This makes it swing...

...until the centre of mass is at its lowest (i.e. directly under the pivot).

Centre of mass

Weight

Pivot

Weight

See page 29 for more on moments.

Note: It rests in this position because there's no moment — the pivot is in line with the line of action of the force.

3) This means you can find the centre of mass of any flat shape like this:

   a) Suspend the shape and a plumb line from the same point, and wait until they stop moving.
   b) Draw a line along the plumb line.
   c) Do the same thing again, but suspend the shape from a different pivot point.
   d) The centre of mass is where your two lines cross.

Picture of snowman.

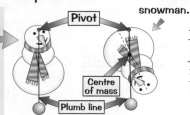

Pivot
Centre of mass
Plumb line

A plumb line is just a mass on the end of a string. When you suspend it, the string becomes perfectly vertical.

4) But you don't need to go to all that trouble for symmetrical shapes. You can quickly guess where the centre of mass is by looking for lines of symmetry.

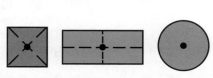

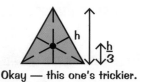

h
$\frac{h}{3}$

Okay — this one's trickier.

Be at the centre of mass — sit on the middle pew...

So there you go, how to find the centre of mass of your favourite piece of irregularly-shaped paper in a few easy steps. You should also now know that the next time someone asks you "How's it hanging?" your response should be "Directly below the point of suspension, thank you for asking". This page truly was an education.

Balanced Moments and Levers

Once you can calculate moments, you can work out if a <u>seesaw is balanced</u>. Useful thing, physics.

A Question of Balance — Are the Moments Equal?

If the <u>anticlockwise moments</u> are equal to the <u>clockwise moments</u>, the object <u>won't turn</u>.

Example 1: Your younger brother weighs <u>300 N</u> and sits <u>2 m</u> from the <u>pivot</u> of a seesaw. If you weigh <u>700 N</u>, where should you sit to <u>balance</u> the seesaw?

For the seesaw to <u>balance</u>:

Total Anticlockwise Moments = Total Clockwise Moments

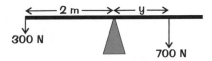

anticlockwise moment = clockwise moment
$$300 \times 2 = 700 \times y$$
$$y = \underline{0.86 \text{ m}}$$

Ignore the weight of the seesaw — its centre of mass is on the pivot, so it doesn't have a turning effect.

Example 2: A <u>6 m</u> long steel girder weighing <u>1000 N</u> rests horizontally on a pole <u>1 m</u> from one end. What is the <u>tension</u> in a supporting cable attached vertically to the other end?

The '<u>tension in the cable</u>' bit makes it sound harder than it actually is.
But the girder's <u>weight</u> is <u>balanced</u> by the tension <u>force</u> in the cable, so...

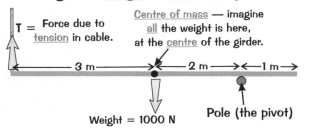

T = Force due to <u>tension</u> in cable.

<u>Centre of mass</u> — imagine <u>all</u> the weight is here, at the <u>centre</u> of the girder.

Weight = 1000 N

Pole (the pivot)

anticlockwise moment = clockwise moment
(due to weight)   (due to tension in cable)
$$1000 \times 2 = T \times 5$$
$$2000 = 5T$$
and so $\underline{T = 400 \text{ N}}$

Simple Levers use Balanced Moments

<u>Levers</u> use the idea of <u>balanced moments</u> to make it <u>easier</u> for us <u>to do work</u> (e.g. <u>lift</u> an object):

1) The <u>moment</u> is equal to <u>force x distance from the pivot</u> (see previous page). So the <u>amount of force</u> needed to produce a particular moment <u>depends</u> on the <u>distance</u> the <u>force</u> is applied from the <u>pivot</u>.

2) Levers <u>increase</u> the <u>distance</u> from the pivot at which the <u>force</u> is applied — so this means <u>less force</u> is needed to get the <u>same moment</u>.

3) That's why levers are known as <u>force multipliers</u> — they <u>reduce</u> the amount of <u>force</u> that's needed to get the <u>same moment</u> by <u>increasing</u> the distance.

Examples of Simple Levers as Force Multipliers

Scissors use a combination of two levers.

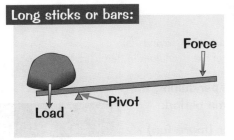

Long sticks or bars:

Force

Pivot

Load

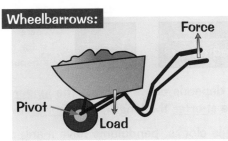

Wheelbarrows:

Force

Pivot

Load

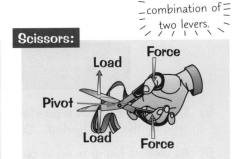

Scissors:

Force

Load

Pivot

Load

Force

These levers make it <u>easier</u> to do <u>work</u> by moving the <u>distance</u> the <u>force</u> is applied <u>further</u> from the pivot.

Balanced moments — nope, not had one of those for a while...

Think of the extra force you need to open a door by pushing it <u>near the hinge</u> compared to <u>at the handle</u> — the <u>distance from the pivot</u> is <u>less</u>, so you need <u>more force</u> to get the <u>same moment</u>. The best way to understand it is to do <u>loads of practice</u>. And make sure you understand the examples of some <u>simple levers</u> from above too.

Moments, Stability and Pendulums

On the last page we met total clockwise moments being balanced by total anticlockwise moments. Which is all <u>very nice and convenient</u>. But what happens if that isn't the case, I hear you cry. Read on my friend...

If the Moments Acting on an Object aren't Equal the Object will Turn

> If the Total Anticlockwise Moments do not equal the Total Clockwise Moments, there will be a Resultant Moment

...so the object will turn.

Low and Wide Objects are Most Stable

<u>Unstable</u> objects tip over easily — <u>stable</u> ones don't. The position of the centre of mass (p.28) is <u>all-important</u>.

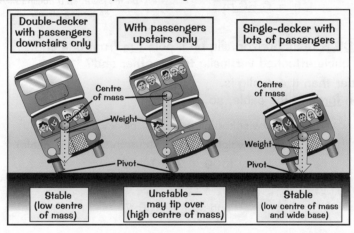

1) The most <u>stable</u> objects have a <u>wide base</u> and a <u>low centre of mass</u>.

2) An object will begin to <u>tip over</u> if its centre of mass moves <u>beyond</u> the edge of its base.

3) Again, it's because of <u>moments</u> — if the <u>line</u> of action of the <u>weight</u> of the object lies <u>outside</u> of the <u>base</u> of the object, it'll cause a <u>resultant moment</u>. This will <u>tip</u> the object over.

4) Lots of objects are specially designed to give them <u>as much stability</u> as possible. For example, a Bunsen burner has a <u>wide</u>, <u>heavy</u> base to give it a <u>low</u> centre of mass — this makes it harder to knock over.

The Time for One Pendulum Swing Depends on its Length

1) A simple <u>pendulum</u> is made by suspending a <u>weight</u> from a piece of <u>string</u>. When you pull back a pendulum and let it go, it will <u>swing</u> back and forth.

2) The time taken for the pendulum to swing from one side to the other and back again is called the <u>time period</u>.

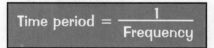

3) The time period for <u>each swing</u> of a given pendulum is always the <u>same</u> — this is what makes pendulums perfect for <u>keeping time</u> in clocks.

4) The time period can be calculated using this <u>formula</u>:

$$\text{Time period} = \frac{1}{\text{Frequency}} \qquad T = \frac{1}{f}$$

Where:
T = the period time in seconds (s)
f = frequency of the pendulum in hertz (Hz)

5) The time period of a pendulum depends on its <u>length</u>. The <u>longer</u> the pendulum, the <u>greater</u> the time period. So the <u>shorter</u> the length, the <u>shorter</u> the time period.

6) As well as being used in old-style clocks, pendulums have many other (more fun) uses. For example, playground <u>swings</u> are pendulums. Any <u>fairground rides</u> that swing you back and forth are pendulums too. Hooray for pendulums.

You are feeling very sleepy, verrrrry sleeeeepy...

So there you go, the science behind the dangers of the age-old, time-passing activity of '<u>stool-swinging</u>'. If the centre of mass of you and the stool falls outside of the stool's base, then you're heading for a fall. Ouch.

Circular Motion

If it wasn't for <u>circular</u> motion our little planet would just be wandering aimlessly around the Universe. And as soon as you launched a <u>satellite</u>, it'd just go flying off into space. Hardly ideal.

Circular Motion — *Velocity is Constantly Changing*

1) <u>Velocity</u> is both the <u>speed</u> and <u>direction</u> of an object (p. 12).

2) If an object is travelling in a circle it is <u>constantly changing direction</u>. This means its <u>velocity</u> is <u>constantly changing</u> (but not its speed) — so the object is <u>accelerating</u> (p. 14). This acceleration is <u>towards</u> the <u>centre</u> of the circle.

3) There must be a <u>resultant force</u> acting on the object causing this acceleration (p. 17). This force acts towards the <u>centre</u> of the circle.

4) This force that keeps something moving in a circle is called a <u>centripetal force</u>.

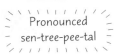

Pronounced sen-tree-pee-tal

The object's acceleration changes the direction of motion but not the speed.

The force causing the acceleration is always towards the centre of the circle.

In the exam, you could be asked to say <u>which force</u> is actually providing the centripetal force in a given situation. It can be <u>tension</u>, or <u>friction</u>, or even <u>gravity</u>.

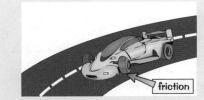

<u>A car going round a bend</u>:

1) Imagine the bend is part of a <u>circle</u> — the centripetal force is towards the <u>centre</u> of the circle.

2) The force is from <u>friction</u> between the car's tyres and the road.

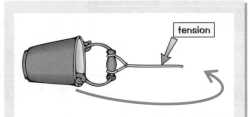

<u>A bucket whirling round on a rope</u>:
The centripetal force comes from <u>tension in the rope</u>. Break the rope, and the bucket flies off at a tangent.

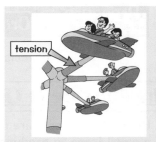

<u>A spinning fairground ride</u>:
The centripetal force comes from <u>tension</u> in the <u>spokes of the ride</u>.

Centripetal Force depends on *Mass, Speed* and *Radius*

1) The <u>faster</u> an object's moving, the <u>bigger</u> the centripetal force has to be to keep it moving in a <u>circle</u>.

2) The <u>larger</u> the <u>mass</u> of the object, the <u>bigger</u> the centripetal force has to be to keep it moving in a <u>circle</u>.

3) And you need a <u>larger force</u> to keep something moving in a <u>smaller circle</u> — it has 'more turning' to do.

Example: Two cars are driving at the same speed around the same circular track. One has a mass of 900 kg, the other has a mass of 1200 kg. Which car has the larger centripetal force?

The <u>three things</u> that mean you need a <u>bigger centripetal force</u> are: <u>more speed</u>, <u>more mass</u>, <u>smaller radius</u> of circle.

In this example, the speed and radius of circle are the same — the <u>only difference</u> is the <u>masses</u> of the cars. So you don't need to calculate anything — you can confidently say:

The <u>1200 kg car</u> (the heavier one) must have the <u>larger centripetal force</u>.

Circular motion — get round to learning it...

To understand this, you need to learn that <u>constant change in direction means constant acceleration</u>. Velocity is a vector — it has direction, and acceleration is change in velocity. When there's acceleration, there's force (see, easy). Learn what forces can provide centripetal force — e.g. tension and friction.

Hydraulics

Oh my word, hydraulics. I have to say that word sounds a <u>little</u> scary, but it's not all that bad really.
It's all just about how we can use the <u>properties of liquids</u> to our advantage. Mwahaha.

Liquids <u>are Virtually</u> Incompressible

1) <u>Liquids</u> are virtually <u>incompressible</u> — you can't <u>squash</u> them, their <u>volume</u> and <u>density</u> stay the <u>same</u>.

2) Because liquids are incompressible and can <u>flow</u>, a <u>force</u> applied to one point
in the liquid will be <u>transmitted</u> (passed) to <u>other points</u> in the liquid.

3) Imagine a <u>balloon</u> full of <u>water</u> with a <u>few holes</u> in it. If you <u>squeeze</u> the <u>top</u> of balloon,
the water will <u>squirt</u> out of the holes. This shows that <u>force applied</u> to the <u>water</u> at
the <u>top</u> of the balloon is transmitted to the <u>water</u> in <u>other parts</u> of the balloon.
This also shows that <u>pressure</u> can be <u>transmitted</u> throughout a liquid.

Pressure and force are linked
— see formula below.

Pressure in a liquid is <u>transmitted equally</u> in <u>all directions</u>.

Pressure <u>is the</u> Force per Unit Area

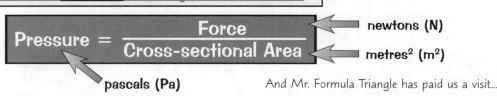

$$\text{Pressure} = \frac{\text{Force}}{\text{Cross-sectional Area}}$$

newtons (N)

metres² (m²)

pascals (Pa)

And Mr. Formula Triangle has paid us a visit...

<u>The Pressure</u> in <u>Liquids</u> can be Used in Hydraulic Systems

1) Hydraulic systems are used as <u>force multipliers</u> — they use
a <u>small force</u> to produce a <u>bigger force</u>. They do this using
<u>liquid</u> and a sneaky trick with <u>cross-sectional areas</u>.

2) The diagram to the right shows a <u>simple hydraulic system</u>.

3) The system has <u>two pistons</u>, one with a <u>smaller</u>
<u>cross-sectional area</u> than the other. Pressure is
transmitted <u>equally</u> through a liquid — so the
pressure at <u>both</u> pistons is the <u>same</u>.

4) <u>Pressure = force ÷ area</u>, so at the <u>1st</u> piston, a pressure is
exerted on the liquid using a <u>small force</u> over a <u>small area</u>.
This pressure is <u>transmitted</u> to the <u>2nd</u> piston.

5) The <u>2nd</u> piston has a <u>larger area</u>, and so as
<u>force = pressure × area</u>, there will be a <u>larger force</u>.

6) Hydraulic systems are used in all sorts of things, e.g. <u>car braking</u> systems,
hydraulic <u>car jacks</u>, <u>manufacturing</u> and deployment of <u>landing gear</u> on some aircraft.

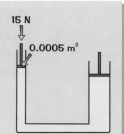

Small force

Piston 1

Small cross-sectional area

Same pressure

Piston 2

Large cross-sectional area

Large force

Liquid

<u>EXAMPLE:</u> To the right is a diagram showing a simple hydraulic system. A force of 15 N
is applied to the first piston which has a cross-sectional area of 0.0005 m².

a) Calculate the pressure created on the first piston.

b) Calculate the force acting on the second piston if its cross-sectional
area is 0.0012 m².

15 N

0.0005 m²

<u>ANSWER:</u> a) P = F ÷ A = 15 ÷ 0.0005 = <u>30 000 Pa</u> (or 30 000 N/m²)

b) Pressure at first piston = pressure at second piston, so
F = P × A = 30 000 × 0.0012 = <u>36 N</u>

<u>With all this talk of hydraulics I'm really feeling under pressure...</u>

See, that wasn't too bad was it? Maybe-ish. Hydraulics is all about using a liquid to make a <u>larger force</u> from
a <u>smaller one</u> (or in some cases vice versa). It's all thanks to those hard-to-compress liquids, with their
pressure-transmitting capabilities. And that's the end of Section One, yey!

Revision Summary for Section One

Well done — you've made it to the end of the first section. There are loads of bits and bobs about forces that you have to learn. The best way to find out what you know is to get stuck in to these lovely revision questions, which you're going to really enjoy (honest)...

1) What's the difference between speed and velocity?
2) Explain how to calculate speed from a distance-time graph.
3)* Write down the formula for acceleration. What's the acceleration of a soggy pea flicked from rest to a speed of 14 m/s in 0.4 seconds?
4) Explain how to find speed, distance and acceleration from a velocity-time graph.
5) If an object has zero resultant force on it, can it be moving?
6)* What's the resultant force of a 120 N force north and a 360 N force south?
7) If an object has zero resultant force on it, can it be accelerating?
8)* Write down the formula relating resultant force and acceleration. A resultant force of 30 N pushes a trolley of mass 4 kg. What will be its acceleration?
9)* A yeti pushes a tree with a force of 120 N. What is the size of the reaction force that the yeti feels pushing back at him?
10) Write down the formula for momentum. If the total momentum of a system before a collision is zero, what is the total momentum of the system after the collision?
11) Explain how seat belts and air bags are useful in a crash.
12) What is "terminal velocity"?
13) What are the two different parts of the overall stopping distance of a car?
14) Explain the difference between mass and weight. What units are they measured in?
15)* Write down the formula for work done. A crazy dog drags a big branch 12 m over the next-door neighbour's front lawn, pulling with a force of 535 N. How much work was done?
16)* A 4 kg cheese is taken 30 m up a hill before being rolled back down again. If g = 10 N/kg, how much gravitational potential energy does the cheese have at the top of the hill?
17)* Find the kinetic energy of a 78 kg sheep moving at 23 m/s.
18)* A car of mass 1000 kg is travelling at a velocity of 2 m/s when a dazed and confused sheep runs out 5 m in front. If the driver immediately applies the maximum braking force of 395 N, can he avoid hitting it?
19) Write down the equation that relates the force on a spring and its extension.
20) What is the limit of proportionality?
21)* Calculate the power output of that 78 kg sheep when she runs 20 m up a staircase in 16.5 seconds.
22) Sarah is levering the lid off a can of paint using a screwdriver. She places the tip of the 20 cm long screwdriver under the can's lid and applies a force of 10 N on the end of the screwdriver's handle. Suggest two ways that Sarah could increase the moment about the pivot point (the side of the can).
23) Describe two different ways of finding the centre of mass of a rectangular playing card.
24)* Arthur weighs 600 N and is sitting on a seesaw 1.5 m from the pivot point. His friend Caroline weighs 450 N and sits on the seesaw so that it balances. How far from the pivot point is Caroline sitting?
25) Give three situations where you use a simple lever.
26)* Calculate the time period of a pendulum swinging with a frequency of 10 Hz.
27) A cyclist is moving at a constant speed of 5 m/s around a circular track.
   a) Is the cyclist accelerating? Explain your answer.
   b) What force keeps the cyclist travelling in a circle? Where does this force come from?
   c) What will happen to the size of this force if the same cyclist travels at a constant speed of 5 m/s around a different circular track that has a larger radius?
28)* A force of 20 N is applied to a piston in a hydraulic system with a cross-sectional area 0.25 m^2. Calculate the pressure applied to the piston.
29) Give one use of a hydraulic system.

* Answers on p.100.

Wave Basics

Waves transfer <u>energy</u> from one place to another without transferring any <u>matter</u> (stuff).

Waves **Have** Amplitude, Wavelength **and** Frequency

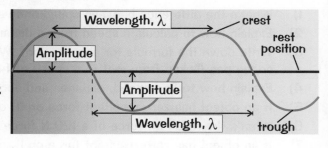

1) The <u>amplitude</u> is the displacement from the <u>rest position</u> to the <u>crest</u> (NOT from a trough to a crest).

2) The <u>wavelength</u> (λ) is the length of a <u>full cycle</u> of the wave, e.g. from <u>crest to crest</u>.

3) <u>Frequency</u> (f) is the <u>number of complete waves</u> passing a certain point <u>per second</u> OR the <u>number of waves</u> produced by a source <u>each second</u>. Frequency is measured in hertz (Hz). 1 Hz is <u>1 wave per second</u>.

4) The <u>period</u> (T) is the <u>time</u> it takes (in <u>s</u>) for <u>one complete wave</u> to pass a point. E.g. a wave with period <u>0.002 s</u> has a frequency of 1 ÷ 0.002 = <u>500 Hz</u>.

$$f = \frac{1}{T}$$

Transverse Waves **Have** Sideways **Oscillations**

<u>Most waves</u> are <u>transverse</u>:
1) <u>Light</u> and <u>all other EM waves</u>.
2) <u>Ripples</u> on water.
3) <u>Waves</u> on <u>strings</u>.
4) A <u>slinky spring</u> wiggled up and down.

In <u>TRANSVERSE</u> waves the oscillations are <u>PERPENDICULAR</u> (at <u>90°</u>) to the <u>DIRECTION OF ENERGY TRANSFER</u> of the wave.

Oscillations from side to side
Wave travelling this way

Longitudinal Waves **Have Oscillations** Along the Same Line

Examples of <u>longitudinal waves</u> are:
1) <u>Sound waves</u> and <u>ultrasound</u>.
2) <u>Shock waves</u>, e.g. seismic waves.
3) A <u>slinky spring</u> when you <u>push</u> the end.

Mechanical waves can be transverse or longitudinal. Water waves, shock waves and waves in springs and ropes are all examples of <u>mechanical waves</u>.

Longitudinal waves <u>squash up</u> and <u>stretch out</u> the arrangement of particles in material they pass through, making <u>compressions</u> and <u>rarefactions</u>. Compressions are the bits under <u>high pressure</u> (lots of particles) and rarefactions are the parts under <u>low pressure</u> (fewer particles).

In <u>LONGITUDINAL</u> waves the oscillations are <u>PARALLEL</u> to the <u>DIRECTION OF ENERGY TRANSFER</u> of the wave.

One wavelength   Rarefactions   Oscillations in same direction as wave is travelling

Compressions

Wave Speed **=** Frequency **×** Wavelength

The equation below applies to <u>all waves</u>. You need to learn it — and <u>practise using it</u>.

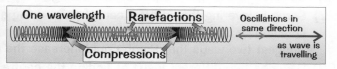

Speed	=	Frequency	×	Wavelength
(m/s)		(Hz)		(m)

OR

$$v = f \times \lambda$$

Wavelength (that's the Greek letter 'lambda')
Speed (v is for <u>velocity</u>)
Frequency

$$\frac{v}{f \times \lambda}$$

<u>EXAMPLE:</u> A radio wave has a frequency of 92.2×10^6 Hz. Find its wavelength. (The speed of all EM waves is 3×10^8 m/s.)

<u>ANSWER:</u> You're trying to find λ using f and v, so you've got to rearrange the equation. So $\lambda = v \div f = 3 \times 10^8 \div 9.22 \times 10^7 = \underline{3.25\ m}$.

Waves — dig the vibes, man...

The first thing to learn is that diagram at the top of the page. Then get that $\underline{v = f \times \lambda}$ business <u>imprinted</u> on your brain. Now try this question: A wave has a frequency of $\underline{1.9 \times 10^4}$ Hz and a wavelength of <u>12.5 cm</u>. Find its speed.*

Reflection of Waves

If you're anything like me, you'll have spent hours gazing into a mirror in <u>wonder</u>. Here's why...

All Waves <u>Can be</u> Reflected, Diffracted <u>and</u> Refracted

1) When waves arrive at an obstacle (or meet a new material), their direction of travel can be changed.
2) This can happen by <u>reflection</u> (see below), <u>diffraction</u> (see page 36), or <u>refraction</u> (see page 37).

Reflection <u>of</u> Light <u>Lets Us See Things</u>

1) <u>Reflection of light</u> is what allows us to <u>see</u> objects. Light bounces off them into our eyes.
2) When light travelling in the <u>same direction</u> reflects from an <u>uneven surface</u> such as a <u>piece of paper</u>, the light reflects off <u>at different angles</u>.
3) When light travelling in the <u>same direction</u> reflects from an <u>even surface</u> (<u>smooth and shiny</u> like a <u>mirror</u>) then it's all reflected at the <u>same angle</u> and you get a <u>clear reflection</u>.

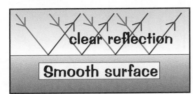

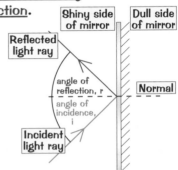

The <u>normal</u> is an imaginary line that's perpendicular (at right angles) to the surface at the point of incidence (where the light hits the surface).

4) The <u>LAW OF REFLECTION</u> applies to <u>every reflected ray</u>:

Angle of <u>INCIDENCE</u> = Angle of <u>REFLECTION</u>

Note that these two angles are <u>ALWAYS</u> defined between the ray itself and the <u>NORMAL</u>, dotted above. <u>Don't ever</u> label them as the angle between the ray and the <u>surface</u>. Definitely uncool.

Draw a <u>Ray Diagram</u> <u>for an Image</u> <u>in a</u> Plane Mirror

You could be asked to draw ray diagrams in the exam.
This one shows <u>how an image is formed</u> in a <u>PLANE MIRROR</u>. Learn these <u>important points</u>:

1) The <u>image</u> is the <u>same size</u> as the <u>object</u>.
2) It is <u>AS FAR BEHIND</u> the mirror as the object is <u>in front</u>.
3) The image is <u>virtual</u> and <u>upright</u>. The image is virtual because the object appears to be <u>behind</u> the mirror.
4) The image is <u>laterally inverted</u> — the left and right sides are <u>swapped</u>, i.e. the object's <u>left</u> side becomes its <u>right</u> side in the <u>image</u>.

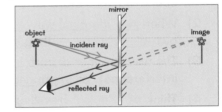

1) First off, draw the <u>virtual image</u>. <u>Don't</u> try to draw the rays first. Follow the rules in the above box — the image is the <u>same size</u>, and it's <u>as far behind</u> the mirror as the object is in <u>front</u>.

2) Next, draw a <u>reflected ray</u> going from the top of the virtual image to the top of the eye. Draw a <u>bold line</u> for the part of the ray between the mirror and eye, and a <u>dotted line</u> for the part of the ray between the mirror and virtual image.

3) Now draw the <u>incident ray</u> going from the top of the object to the mirror. The incident and reflected rays follow the <u>law of reflection</u> — but you <u>don't</u> actually have to measure any angles. Just draw the ray from the <u>object</u> to the <u>point</u> where the reflected ray <u>meets the mirror</u>.

4) Now you have an <u>incident ray</u> and <u>reflected ray</u> for the <u>top</u> of the image. Do <u>steps 2 and 3 again</u> for the <u>bottom</u> of the <u>eye</u> — a reflected ray going from the image to the bottom of the eye, then an incident ray from the object to the mirror.

Plane mirrors — what pilots use to look behind them...

Make sure you can draw clear <u>ray diagrams</u> and you'll be well on your way to picking up lotsa marks in the exam.

Diffraction and Interference

If you thought <u>reflection</u> was good, you'll love <u>diffraction</u> and <u>interference</u> — they're awesome. If you didn't find reflection interesting then I'm afraid it's tough luck — you need to know about these anyway. Sorry.

Diffraction — *Waves Spreading Out*

1) All waves <u>spread out</u> ('<u>diffract</u>') at the edges when they pass through a <u>gap</u> or <u>pass an object</u>.
2) The <u>amount</u> of diffraction depends on the <u>size</u> of the gap relative to the <u>wavelength</u> of the wave.
3) The <u>narrower the gap</u>, or the <u>longer the wavelength</u>, the <u>more</u> the wave spreads out.
4) A <u>narrow gap</u> is one about the same size as the <u>wavelength</u> of the wave.
   So whether a gap counts as narrow or not depends on the wave.

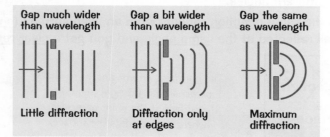

5) <u>Light</u> has a very <u>small wavelength</u> (about 0.0005 mm), so it can be diffracted but it needs a <u>really small gap</u>.
6) This means you can <u>hear</u> someone through an open door even if you <u>can't see them</u>, because the <u>size of the gap</u> and the <u>wavelength of sound</u> are roughly <u>equal</u>, causing the sound wave to <u>diffract</u> and fill the room...
7) ...But you <u>can't see them</u> unless you're <u>directly facing</u> the door because the gap is about a <u>million</u> times <u>bigger</u> than the <u>wavelength</u> of <u>light</u>, so it <u>won't</u> diffract enough.

When *Identical* Sets of Waves *Meet They* Interfere With Each Other

1) All waves cause some kind of <u>disturbance</u> in a medium — water waves disturb water particles, sound waves disturb air particles, electromagnetic waves disturb electric and magnetic fields.
2) When <u>two identical waves meet</u> at a point they both try to cause their own <u>disturbance</u> — they <u>interfere</u> with each other.
3) The waves either disturb in the <u>same direction</u> and <u>reinforce</u> each other (<u>constructive</u> interference), or in <u>opposite directions</u> and <u>cancel</u> each other out (<u>destructive</u> interference).
4) Think of a '<u>pulse</u>' travelling down a slinky spring meeting a pulse travelling in the opposite direction. These diagrams show the <u>possible outcomes</u>: ⟹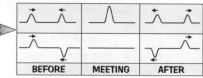
5) The <u>total displacement</u> of the waves at a point is the <u>sum</u> of the <u>displacements</u> (you have to take direction into account) of the waves at that point.

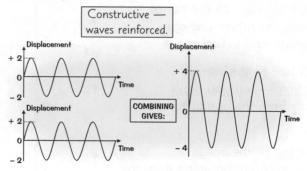

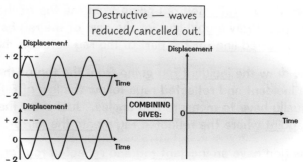

Destructive interference — too many cooks spoil the wave...

It's weird, isn't it... I mean, <u>constructive</u> interference makes perfect <u>sense</u> — two waves, bigger sound... it's just <u>destructive</u> interference that gets me. I know WHY it happens... but I still find it <u>weird</u>.

Refraction of Waves

All waves can be <u>refracted</u> — it's a fancy way of saying '<u>change direction</u>'.

Waves Can be <u>Refracted</u>

1) Waves travel at <u>different speeds</u> in substances which have <u>different densities</u>. EM waves travel more <u>slowly</u> in <u>denser</u> media (usually). Sound waves travel faster in <u>denser</u> substances.

2) So when a wave crosses a boundary between two substances, from glass to air, say, it <u>changes speed</u>.

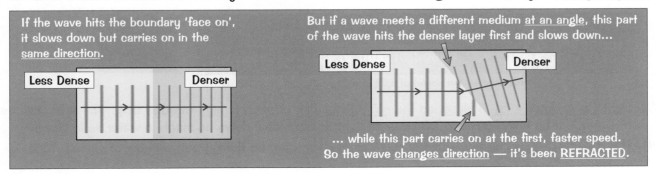

3) When light enters a <u>more dense</u> medium it <u>slows down</u> and <u>refracts towards</u> the normal. When it enters a <u>less dense</u> medium it <u>speeds up</u> and <u>refracts away</u> from the normal.

4) You can <u>experiment</u> with refraction using a light source and a <u>rectangular block</u> of a particular material (e.g. glass) resting on top of a piece of paper...

5) Shine a light ray at an angle into the block, as shown. Some of the light is reflected, but a lot of it passes through the glass and gets <u>refracted</u> as it does so.

6) <u>Trace</u> the <u>incident</u> and <u>emergent</u> rays onto the piece of paper and remove the block. You can <u>draw in</u> the <u>refracted ray</u> through the block by joining the ends of the other two rays with a straight line.

7) You should see that as the light passes from the air into the block, it bends <u>towards</u> the normal.

8) When the light reaches the boundary on the other side of the block, it bends <u>away</u> from the normal.
(Some of the light is also <u>reflected</u> at this boundary.)

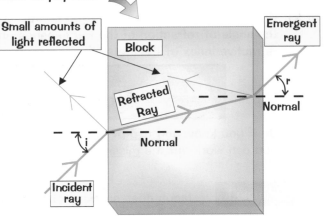

9) The light ray that emerges on the other side of the block is now travelling in the <u>same direction</u> it was to begin with — it's been <u>refracted</u> towards the normal and then back again by the <u>same amount</u>.

10) You can <u>measure the angles</u> between the rays and the normal to work out the <u>refractive index</u> of the material in the block (see next page).

Triangular <u>Prisms Disperse</u> <u>White Light</u>

<u>Different wavelengths</u> of light refract by <u>different amounts</u>, so <u>white light</u> disperses into <u>different colours</u> as it <u>enters a prism</u>. A <u>rectangular</u> block has parallel boundaries, so the rays bend by the <u>same amount</u> when they leave the block as when they entered — so <u>white light emerges</u>. But with a <u>triangular</u> prism, the boundaries aren't parallel, which means the <u>different wavelengths</u> don't recombine, and you get a nice <u>rainbow effect</u>.

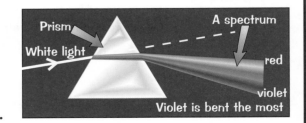

Denser media — lead newspapers...

Learn the straightforward rule: <u>more dense</u> materials <u>slow light down</u> so it bends <u>towards</u> the normal, <u>less dense</u> materials <u>speed it up</u> so it bends <u>away</u> from the normal.

Refractive Index

So you're <u>totally happy</u> with the last page. And you're <u>sure</u> about that. Good. Gets a bit hairy here...

Every Transparent Material Has a Refractive Index

1) The <u>refractive index</u> of a <u>transparent material</u> tells you <u>how fast</u> light travels in that material.

2) The <u>refractive index</u> of a material is the ratio of the speed of light in a vacuum to the speed of light in that material:

$$\text{refractive index, } n = \frac{\text{speed of light in a vacuum, c}}{\text{speed of light in that material, v}} \qquad n = \frac{c}{v}$$

(Remember — the speed of light in a vacuum, $c = 3 \times 10^8$ m/s)

3) Light <u>slows down a lot</u> in <u>glass</u>, so the <u>refractive index</u> of glass is <u>high</u> (around 1.5). The refractive index of <u>water</u> is a bit <u>lower</u> (around 1.33) — so light doesn't slow down as much in water as in glass.

4) The <u>speed of light in air</u> is about the <u>same</u> as in a <u>vacuum</u>, so the <u>refractive index</u> of <u>air</u> is 1 (to 2 d.p.).

You can Calculate Refractive Index a Second Way

1) The <u>angle of incidence</u>, <u>angle of refraction</u> and <u>refractive index</u> are all <u>linked</u>.

2) When an incident ray passes <u>from air</u> into <u>another material</u>, the angle of refraction of the ray depends upon the refractive index of the material:

$$\text{refractive index } (n) = \frac{\sin i}{\sin r}$$

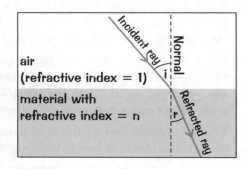

air
(refractive index = 1)

material with
refractive index = n

3) So if you know <u>any two</u> of <u>n</u>, <u>i</u> or <u>r</u>, you can work out the <u>missing one</u>.

Example 1

Jacob does an experiment to find out the refractive index of his strawberry flavour jelly. He finds that when the angle of incidence for a light beam travelling into his jelly is <u>42°</u>, the angle of refraction is <u>35°</u>. What is the <u>refractive index</u> of this particular type of jelly?

$$n = \frac{\sin i}{\sin r} \qquad \sin i = \sin 42 = 0.67 \qquad \sin r = \sin 35 = 0.57 \implies \text{so } n_{jelly} = \frac{0.67}{0.57} = \underline{1.18}$$

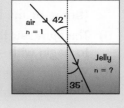

air
n = 1

Jelly
n = ?

42°

35°

Example 2

A beam of light travels from air into water (refractive index <u>n = 1.33</u>). The angle of incidence is <u>23°</u>. Calculate the angle of refraction to the nearest degree.

$$\sin r = \frac{\sin i}{n} = \frac{\sin 23}{1.33} = 0.29 \implies \text{so } r = \sin^{-1}(0.29) = \underline{17°}$$

normal

air

water

Revise refraction — but don't let it slow you down...

There's not tooooo much to learn here — just make sure you know the <u>formulas</u> and what <u>refractive index</u> is. If you forget <u>which way up</u> either of the formulas are supposed to go, just remember that <u>n will be greater than 1</u> for most materials, and you should be able to figure it out. Easy-peasy, cheddar-cheesy.

Total Internal Reflection

Total internal reflection is a special case of refraction (even if the name makes it sound otherwise).

Light can be Sent Along Optical Fibres Using Total Internal Reflection

1) Optical fibres can carry visible light over long distances (see p. 41).

2) They work by bouncing waves off the sides of a thin inner core of glass or plastic. The wave enters one end of the fibre and is reflected repeatedly until it emerges at the other end.

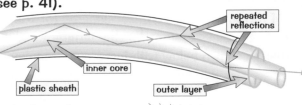

3) Optical fibres work because of total internal reflection.

4) Total internal reflection can only happen when a wave travels through a dense substance like glass or water towards a less dense substance like air.

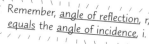

Remember, angle of reflection, r, equals the angle of incidence, i.

5) It all depends on whether the angle of incidence is bigger than the critical angle...

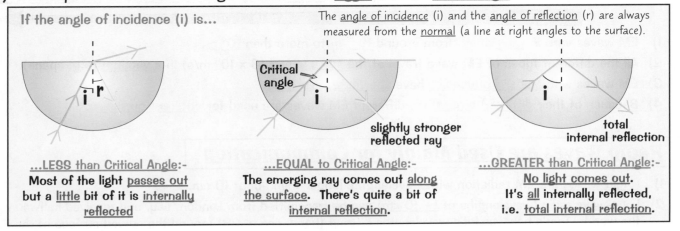

If the angle of incidence (i) is...

The angle of incidence (i) and the angle of reflection (r) are always measured from the normal (a line at right angles to the surface).

Critical angle

slightly stronger reflected ray

total internal reflection

...LESS than Critical Angle:-
Most of the light passes out but a little bit of it is internally reflected

...EQUAL to Critical Angle:-
The emerging ray comes out along the surface. There's quite a bit of internal reflection.

...GREATER than Critical Angle:-
No light comes out.
It's all internally reflected, i.e. total internal reflection.

The Value of the Critical Angle Depends on the Refractive Index

1) A dense material with a high refractive index (see p.38) has a low critical angle.

2) If a material has a high refractive index, it will totally internally reflect more light — more light will be incident at an angle bigger than the critical angle.

3) For example, the critical angle of glass is around 42°, but for diamond the critical angle is just 24°, so more light is totally internally reflected — which is why diamonds are so sparkly.

4) Refractive index and critical angle (c) are related by this formula:

$$\text{Refractive index} = \frac{1}{\sin c}$$

Endoscopes Use Bundles of Optical Fibres

1) An endoscope is a thin tube containing optical fibres that lets surgeons examine inside the body.

2) Endoscopes consist of two bundles of optical fibres — one to carry light to the area of interest and one to carry an image back so that it can be viewed.

Optical fibres

Light source   Endoscope

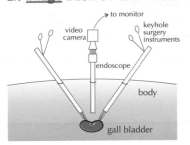

to monitor
video camera
keyhole surgery instruments
endoscope
body
gall bladder

3) The image can be seen through an eyepiece or displayed as a full-colour moving image on a TV screen.

4) The big advantage of using endoscopes is that surgeons can now perform many operations by only cutting teeny holes in people — this is called keyhole surgery, and it wasn't possible before optical fibres.

Internally reflect on this a while...

Sure, endoscopes are useful for medicine, but I use mine to see when dinner's ready from the comfort of my bed...

Electromagnetic Waves and Their Uses

Types of <u>electromagnetic</u> (EM) wave have a lot in common with one another, but their <u>differences</u> make them useful to us in different ways. These pages are packed with loads of dead important info, so pay attention...

There's a Continuous Spectrum of EM Waves

EM waves with <u>different wavelengths</u> (or frequencies) have different properties. We group them into <u>seven basic types</u>, but the different regions actually merge to form a <u>continuous spectrum</u>.

They're shown below with increasing frequency and energy (decreasing wavelength) from left to right.

	RADIO WAVES	MICRO WAVES	INFRA RED	VISIBLE LIGHT	ULTRA VIOLET	X-RAYS	GAMMA RAYS
wavelength →	$1\ m - 10^4\ m$	$10^{-2}\ m$ (1 cm)	$10^{-5}\ m$ (0.01 mm)	$10^{-7}\ m$	$10^{-8}\ m$	$10^{-10}\ m$	$10^{-15}\ m$

INCREASING FREQUENCY AND ENERGY **AND** DECREASING WAVELENGTH ➡️

1) EM waves vary in <u>wavelength</u> from around $10^{-15}\ m$ to more than $10^4\ m$.
2) All the different types of EM wave travel at the <u>same speed</u> (3×10^8 m/s) in a <u>vacuum</u> (e.g. space).
3) EM waves with <u>higher frequencies</u> have <u>shorter wavelengths</u>.
4) Because of their <u>different properties</u>, different EM waves are used for <u>different purposes</u>.

Radio Waves are Used Mainly for Communication

1) <u>Radio waves</u> are EM radiation with wavelengths longer than about 10 cm.
2) <u>Long-wave radio</u> (wavelengths of <u>1 – 10 km</u>) can be transmitted from London, say, and received halfway round the world. That's because long wavelengths <u>diffract</u> (<u>bend</u>, see p. 36) around the curved surface of the Earth.

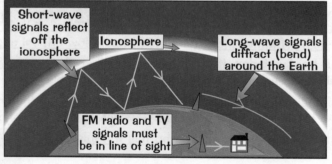

Short-wave signals reflect off the ionosphere
Ionosphere
Long-wave signals diffract (bend) around the Earth
FM radio and TV signals must be in line of sight

Microwaves, infrared and visible light can all be used for communications too — see next page.

3) <u>Long-wave radio</u> wavelengths can also <u>diffract</u> around <u>hills</u>, into <u>tunnels</u> and all sorts.
4) This <u>diffraction effect</u> makes it possible for radio signals to be <u>received</u> even if the receiver <u>isn't</u> in <u>line of the sight</u> of the <u>transmitter</u>.
5) The radio waves used for <u>TV and FM radio</u> transmissions have very short wavelengths (10 cm – 10 m). To get reception, you must be in <u>direct sight of the transmitter</u> because the signal doesn't bend.
6) <u>Short-wave radio</u> signals (wavelengths of about <u>10 m – 100 m</u>) can, like long-wave, be received at <u>long distances</u> from the transmitter. That's because they are <u>reflected</u> (see p. 35) from the <u>ionosphere</u> — an <u>electrically charged layer</u> in the Earth's upper atmosphere.
7) <u>Bluetooth</u>® uses short-wave radio waves to send data over short distances between devices <u>without wires</u>.
8) <u>Medium-wave</u> signals (well, the shorter ones) can also reflect from the ionosphere, depending on atmospheric conditions and the time of day.

Size matters — and my wave's longer than yours...

You'll have to be able to <u>name</u> the <u>order</u> of the different types of EM waves in terms of their <u>energy</u>, <u>frequency</u> and <u>wavelength</u>. To remember the order of <u>increasing frequency</u> and <u>energy</u>, I use the mnemonic <u>R</u>ock <u>M</u>usic <u>I</u>s <u>V</u>ery <u>U</u>seful for e<u>X</u>periments with <u>G</u>oats. It sounds stupid but it <u>does</u> work — why not make up your own...

Electromagnetic Waves and Their Uses

Radio waves aren't the only waves used for communication — other EM waves come in pretty handy too. The most important thing is to think about how the properties of a wave relate to its uses.

Microwaves are Used for Satellite Communication and Mobile Phones

microwaves
clouds and water vapour

1) Communication to and from satellites (including satellite TV signals and satellite phones) uses microwaves. But you need to use microwaves which can pass easily through the Earth's watery atmosphere. Radio waves can't do this.

2) For satellite TV, the signal from a transmitter is transmitted into space...

3) ... where it's picked up by the satellite's receiver dish orbiting thousands of kilometres above the Earth. The satellite transmits the signal back to Earth in a different direction...

4) ... where it's received by a satellite dish on the ground.

5) Mobile phone calls also travel as microwaves between your phone and the nearest transmitter. Some wavelengths of microwaves are absorbed by water molecules and heat them up. If the water in question happens to be in your cells, you might start to cook — so some people think using your mobile a lot (especially next to your head), or living near a mast, could damage your health. There isn't any conclusive evidence either way yet.

6) And microwaves are used by remote-sensing satellites — to 'see' through the clouds and monitor oil spills, track the movement of icebergs, see how much rainforest has been chopped down and so on.

Infrared Waves are Used for Remote Controls and Optical Fibres

1) Infrared waves are used in lots of wireless remote controllers.
2) Remote controls work by emitting different patterns of infrared waves to send different commands to an appliance, e.g. a TV.

3) Optical fibres (e.g. those used in phone lines) can carry data over long distances very quickly.
4) They use both infrared waves and visible light.
5) The signal is carried as pulses of light or infrared radiation and is reflected off the sides of a very narrow core from one end of the fibre to the other (see p. 39).

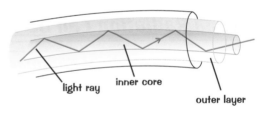
light ray   inner core   outer layer

Visible Light is Useful for Photography

It sounds pretty obvious, but photography would be kinda tricky without visible light.

1) Cameras use a lens to focus visible light onto a light-sensitive film or electronic sensor.
2) The lens aperture controls how much light enters the camera (like the pupil in an eye).
3) The shutter speed determines how long the film or sensor is exposed to the light.
4) By varying the aperture and shutter speed (and also the sensitivity of the film or the sensor), a photographer can capture as much or as little light as they want in their photograph.

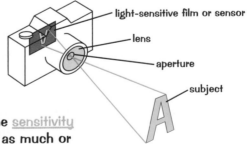
light-sensitive film or sensor
lens
aperture
subject

Microwaves are also used for making popcorn — mmm...

I bet you didn't realise that all those different types of technology — like microwaves and infrared — use waves that travel at exactly the same speed as each other (in a vacuum). It's pretty cool stuff.

Electromagnetic Waves and Their Uses

That's right — <u>yet another page</u> on the <u>uses of EM waves</u>. <u>Ultraviolet</u>, <u>X-rays</u> and <u>gamma rays</u> are the <u>shortest</u> waves in the spectrum, and we use them for <u>all sorts</u> of fancy stuff...

Ultraviolet Radiation *is Used for Security* Marking

1) <u>Fluorescence</u> is a property of certain chemicals, where <u>ultraviolet radiation (UV)</u> is <u>absorbed</u> and then <u>visible light</u> is <u>emitted</u>. That's why fluorescent colours look so <u>bright</u> — they do actually <u>emit light</u>.

2) <u>Banks</u> now print <u>special markings</u> in <u>fluorescent ink</u> on their <u>bank notes</u> to detect <u>forgeries</u>. <u>Under a UV light</u>, <u>genuine</u> notes will <u>display</u> the special <u>fluorescent markings</u>... <u>Fake</u> notes, on the other hand, are often printed on <u>cheaper paper</u> that's <u>slightly fluorescent</u>, so under UV, they'll <u>glow all over</u>, and there'll be <u>no markings</u>.

3) Here, it's the amount of radiation <u>emitted</u> that you're detecting and measuring.

4) <u>Security pens</u> can be used to <u>mark</u> your property with your name (e.g. laptops). The ink in the pen is only visible in <u>UV light</u> — this can help the police <u>identify</u> your property if it's stolen.

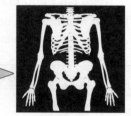

X-Rays *Let Us See Inside* Things

1) <u>X-rays</u> are used to view the <u>internal structure</u> of <u>objects</u> and <u>materials</u>, including our <u>bodies</u> — which is why they're so useful in <u>medicine</u>.

2) To produce an <u>X-ray image</u>, X-ray radiation is directed <u>through the object</u> or body onto a <u>detector plate</u>. The <u>brighter bits</u> are where <u>fewer X-rays</u> get through. This is a <u>negative image</u>. The plate starts off <u>all white</u>.

3) <u>Radiographers</u> in <u>hospitals</u> take <u>X-ray photographs</u> to help doctors diagnose <u>broken bones</u> — X-rays pass <u>easily through</u> <u>flesh</u> but not through <u>denser material</u> like <u>bones</u> or metal.

4) Because exposure to X-rays can cause <u>mutations</u> which lead to <u>cancer</u>, radiographers and patients are <u>protected</u> as much as possible by <u>lead aprons</u> and <u>shields</u>, and exposure to the radiation is kept to a <u>minimum</u>.

See p.44 for more on x-rays in medicine.

Gamma *Radiation Can be Very Useful For...*

...Sterilising Medical Equipment

1) Gamma rays are used to <u>sterilise</u> medical instruments by <u>killing</u> all the microbes.

2) This is better than trying to <u>boil</u> plastic instruments, which might be <u>damaged</u> by high temperatures.

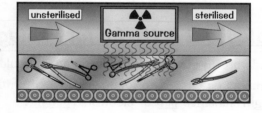

...Sterilising Food

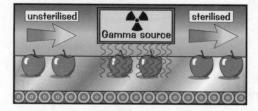

1) <u>Food</u> can be sterilised in the same way as medical instruments — again <u>killing</u> all the <u>microbes</u> (including bacteria).

2) This keeps the food <u>fresh for longer</u>, without having to freeze it or cook it or preserve it some other way.

3) The food is <u>not</u> radioactive afterwards, so it's <u>perfectly safe</u> to eat.

Don't lie to radiographers — they can see right through you...

You've probably got the idea by now that we use electromagnetic radiation an awful lot — much more even than the few examples covered on the last few pages. These are the uses you need to make sure you know for the exam though, so <u>close the book</u>, pick up a pen and <u>write down</u> the uses for <u>all seven types of EM wave</u>.

Dangers of Electromagnetic Waves

Okay, so you know how useful electromagnetic radiation can be — well, it can also be pretty dangerous.

Some EM Radiation Can be Harmful to People

When EM radiation enters living tissue — like you — it's often harmless, but sometimes it creates havoc.

1) Some EM radiation mostly passes through soft tissue without being absorbed — e.g. radio waves.

2) Other types of radiation are absorbed and cause heating of the cells — e.g. microwaves.

3) Some radiations (UV, X-rays and gamma) are ionising — when they enter living cells they collide with atoms in molecules, knocking electrons off and causing ionisation. This damages or destroys the cells. Lower doses tend to cause minor damage without killing the cell, but this can lead to tissue damage, or cell mutation and cancer. Higher doses can kill the cells completely, causing radiation sickness.

Higher Frequency EM Radiation is Usually More Dangerous

1) The effects of EM radiation depend on its frequency. The higher the frequency of EM radiation, the more energy it has and generally the more harmful it can be.

2) In general, waves with lower frequencies (like radio waves — which are harmless as far as we know) are less harmful than high frequency waves like X-rays and gamma rays.

3) From a safety point of view, it's how radiation affects human tissue that's most vital. You need to know how the body can be affected if exposed to too much of the following radiation:

MICROWAVES
Microwaves have a similar frequency to the vibrations of many molecules, and so they can increase these vibrations. The result is internal heating — the heating of molecules inside things (as in microwave ovens). Microwaves HEAT HUMAN BODY TISSUE internally in this way. Microwave ovens need to have shielding to prevent microwaves from reaching the user.

INFRARED
The infrared (IR) range of frequencies can make the surface molecules of any substance vibrate — and like microwaves, this has a heating effect. But infrared has a higher frequency, so it carries more energy than microwave radiation. If the human body is exposed to too much infrared radiation, it can cause some nasty SKIN BURNS. You can protect yourself using insulating materials to reduce the amount of IR reaching your skin.

ULTRAVIOLET
UV radiation can DAMAGE SURFACE CELLS and cause BLINDNESS. It's 'ionising' — it carries enough energy to knock electrons off atoms. This can cause cell mutation or destruction, and can cause skin cancer (see above). You should wear sunscreen with UV filters whenever you're out in the sun, and stay out of strong sunlight to protect your skin from UV radiation.

X-RAYS / GAMMA
Very high-frequency waves, such as gamma rays and X-rays, are also ionising, and carry much more energy than UV rays. This means they can be much more damaging and they can penetrate further into the body. Like all ionising radiation, they can cause GENETIC MUTATION or destruction, leading to TISSUE DAMAGE or CANCER. Radioactive sources of gamma rays should be kept in lead-lined boxes when not in use. When people need to be exposed to them, e.g. in medical treatment, the exposure time should be as short as possible.

(Left margin: INCREASING FREQUENCY — with downward arrow)

I'll have the gamma and chips please, save the pineapple...

There's no point being paranoid — a little bit of sunshine won't kill you (in fact it'll probably do you good). But don't be daft... getting cancer from sunbathing for hours on end is just stupid. It's all a case of balancing the risks against the benefits, as well as keeping unnecessary exposure to a minimum.

X-Rays

X-rays are ionising — they can damage living cells (see p. 43) but they can be really useful if <u>handled carefully</u>...

X-ray Images <u>are Used in</u> Hospitals <u>for</u> Medical Diagnosis

1) <u>X-rays</u> are <u>high-frequency</u>, <u>high-energy</u>, <u>short-wavelength electromagnetic waves</u> (see p. 40).

2) They are <u>transmitted</u> by (pass through) <u>healthy soft tissue</u>, but are absorbed by <u>denser materials</u> like <u>bones</u> and <u>metal</u>.

3) They affect <u>photographic</u> film in the same way as <u>light</u>, which means they can be used to take photographs.

4) <u>X-ray photographs</u> can be used to diagnose many medical conditions such as <u>bone fractures</u> or <u>dental problems</u> (problems with your teeth).

5) X-ray images can also be formed <u>electronically</u> using <u>charge-coupled devices</u> (CCDs).

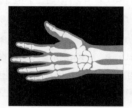

This is a <u>negative image</u>. The plate starts off <u>all white</u>. The <u>brighter bits</u> are where <u>fewer X-rays</u> get through.

CT Scans <u>use X-rays</u>

<u>Computed tomography</u> (CT) scans use X-rays to produce <u>high resolution images</u> of soft and hard tissue.
The patient is put inside the cylindrical scanner, and an X-ray beam is fired through the body from an <u>X-ray tube</u> and picked up by <u>detectors</u> on the opposite side.
The X-ray tube and detectors are <u>rotated</u> during the scan.
A computer interprets the signals from the detectors to form an image of a <u>two-dimensional slice</u> through the body.
Multiple two-dimensional CT scans can be put together to make a <u>three-dimensional image</u> of the inside of the body.

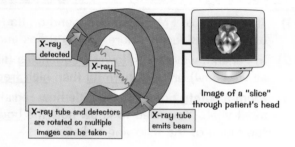

Image of a "slice" through patient's head

Soft tissue can absorb a small amount of X-ray radiation. CT scans use lots of X-rays (more than normal X-ray photographs) to distinguish between the tiny variations in tissue density.

X-rays can be Used to Treat Cancer

X-rays can cause <u>ionisation</u> (see p. 43), so high doses of X-rays will <u>kill living cells</u>. This means they can be used to <u>treat cancer</u>. The X-rays have to be <u>carefully focused</u> and at just the right <u>dosage</u> to kill the <u>cancer cells</u> without damaging too many <u>normal cells</u>.

TO TREAT CANCER:

1) The X-rays are <u>focused</u> on the tumour using a <u>wide beam</u>.

2) This beam is <u>rotated</u> round the patient with the tumour at the centre.

3) This <u>minimises</u> the exposure of <u>normal cells</u> to radiation, and so <u>reduces</u> the chances of damaging the rest of the body.

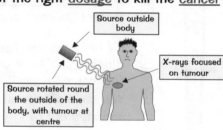

Source outside body

X-rays focused on tumour

Source rotated round the outside of the body, with tumour at centre

Radiographers <u>Take</u> Precautions <u>to</u> Minimise Radiation Dose

Prolonged exposure to ionising radiation can be very dangerous to your health.

1) <u>Radiographers</u> who work with <u>X-ray machines</u> or <u>CT scanners</u> need to take precautions to <u>minimise</u> their <u>X-ray dose</u> (how much they're exposed to).

2) They wear <u>lead aprons</u>, stand behind a <u>lead screen</u>, or <u>leave the room</u> while scans are being done.

3) Lead is also used to <u>shield</u> areas of the patient's body that aren't being scanned, and the <u>exposure time</u> to the X-rays is always kept to an absolute <u>minimum</u>.

Don't just scan this page — focus on it...

As well as having lead aprons and screens to stand behind, radiographers wear special <u>badges</u> that record the amount of radiation they are exposed to. This means that their <u>radiation dose</u> can be <u>monitored</u> and <u>regulated</u>.

Sound and Ultrasound

We hear sounds when <u>vibrations</u> reach our <u>eardrums</u>. You'll need to know how sound waves work.

Sound Travels as a Wave

1) <u>Sound waves</u> are caused by <u>vibrating objects</u>. These mechanical vibrations are passed through the surrounding medium as a series of compressions. They're a type of <u>longitudinal wave</u> (see page 34).

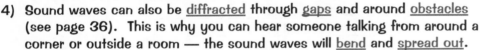

compressions

Vibrations of particles

Direction of sound wave — same direction as vibrations

2) Sometimes the sound will eventually travel through someone's <u>ear</u> and reach their <u>eardrum</u>, at which point the person might <u>hear it</u>.

3) Sound generally travels <u>faster in solids</u> than in liquids, and faster in liquids than in gases.

4) Sound can't travel in <u>space</u>, because it's mostly a <u>vacuum</u> (there are no particles).

Sound Waves Can Reflect, Refract and Diffract

1) Sound waves will be <u>reflected</u> by <u>hard flat surfaces</u>. Things like <u>carpets</u> and <u>curtains</u> act as <u>absorbing surfaces</u> which will <u>absorb</u> sounds rather than reflect them.

2) <u>Echoes</u> are just <u>reflected</u> sound waves — they take <u>longer</u> to reach your ears than the original sound because they had <u>further</u> to travel.

3) <u>Sound waves</u> will also <u>refract</u> (change direction) as they enter <u>different media</u>. As they enter <u>denser</u> material, they <u>speed up</u>.

(However, since sound waves are always <u>spreading out so much</u>, the change in direction is <u>hard to spot</u> under normal circumstances.)

Sound waves

Air

Water

4) Sound waves can also be <u>diffracted</u> through <u>gaps</u> and around <u>obstacles</u> (see page 36). This is why you can hear someone talking from around a corner or outside a room — the sound waves will <u>bend</u> and <u>spread out</u>.

The Higher the Frequency, the Higher the Pitch

1) <u>High frequency</u> sound waves sound <u>high pitched</u> like a <u>squeaking mouse</u>.

2) <u>Low frequency</u> sound waves sound <u>low pitched</u> like a <u>mooing cow</u>.

3) <u>Frequency</u> is the number of <u>complete vibrations</u> each second — so a wave that has a frequency of 100 Hz vibrates 100 times each second.

4) <u>Humans</u> can typically hear from about <u>20 Hz to 20 000 Hz</u>.

5) <u>High frequency</u> (or high pitch) also means <u>shorter wavelength</u> (see p. 34).

6) The <u>loudness</u> of a sound depends on the <u>amplitude</u> (p. 34) of the sound wave. The <u>bigger</u> the amplitude, the <u>louder</u> the sound.

Ultrasound is Sound with a Higher Frequency than We Can Hear

Electrical systems can be made which produce <u>electrical oscillations</u> of <u>any frequency</u>. These can easily be converted into <u>mechanical vibrations</u> to produce <u>sound</u> (acoustic) waves of a <u>higher frequency</u> than the <u>upper limit of human hearing</u> (the range of human hearing is 20 to 20 000 Hz). This is called <u>ultrasound</u>, and there's a lot more on it on the next page.

The room always feels big and empty whenever I tell a joke... (It must be the carpets.)

The thing to do here is learn the facts. There's a simple equation that says <u>the more you learn now</u>, the <u>more marks you'll get</u> in the exam. A lot of questions just test whether you've learnt the facts. Easy marks, really.

More on Ultrasound

As promised, a whole load more on ultrasound...

Ultrasound Waves Get Partially Reflected at a Boundary Between Media

1) When a wave passes from one medium into another, <u>some</u> of the wave is <u>reflected</u> off the boundary between the two media, and some is transmitted (and refracted). This is <u>partial reflection</u>.

2) What this means is that you can point a pulse of ultrasound at an object, and wherever there are <u>boundaries</u> between one substance and another, some of the ultrasound gets <u>reflected back</u>.

3) The time taken for reflections to reach a <u>detector</u> can be used to calculate <u>how far away</u> the boundary is. This is how <u>ultrasound imaging</u> works.

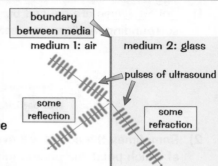

You Can Use Oscilloscope Traces to Find Boundaries

1) The oscilloscope trace on the right shows an ultrasound pulse reflecting off <u>two separate boundaries</u>.

2) Given the "seconds per division" setting of the oscilloscope (see p.73), you can work out the <u>time</u> between pulses by measuring on the screen.

3) If you know the <u>speed of sound</u> in the medium, you can work out the <u>distance</u> between the boundaries, using this formula:
s is <u>distance</u> in metres, m.
v is <u>speed</u> in metres per second, m/s.
t is <u>time</u> in seconds, s.

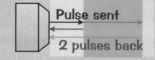

$$s = v \times t$$

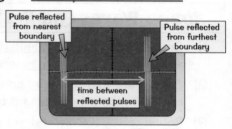

Example: A pulse of ultrasound is beamed into a patient's abdomen. The first boundary it reflects off is between fat and muscle. The second boundary is between muscle and a body cavity. An oscilloscope trace shows that the <u>time between the reflected pulses</u> is <u>10 μs</u>. The ultrasound travels at a <u>speed</u> of <u>1500 m/s</u>. Calculate the <u>distance</u> between the fat/muscle boundary and the muscle/cavity boundary.

1 μs = 0.000001 s

So, you'll need to find the distance using s = v × t.
BUT, the reflected pulses have travelled <u>there and back</u>, so the distance you calculate will be <u>twice the distance between boundaries</u> (think about it).
s = v × t = 1500 × 0.00001 = 0.015 m.
So the distance between boundaries = 0.015 ÷ 2 = 0.0075 m = <u>7.5 mm</u>.

Pulse sent

2 pulses back

Ultrasound Waves can be Used in Medicine

<u>Ultrasound</u> has a variety of uses in medicine. The examples below are two of the <u>most common</u>:

1) <u>Kidney stones</u> are <u>hard masses</u> that can <u>block</u> the <u>urinary tract</u> — ouch. An ultrasound beam concentrates <u>high-energy waves</u> at the kidney stone and turns it into <u>sand-like particles</u>. These particles then pass out of the body in the <u>urine</u>. It's a good method because the patient <u>doesn't need surgery</u> and it's relatively <u>painless</u>.

2) <u>Ultrasound waves</u> can pass through the body, but whenever they reach a <u>boundary</u> between <u>two different media</u> (like fluid in the womb and the skin of a fetus) some of the wave is <u>reflected back</u> and <u>detected</u>. The exact <u>timing and distribution</u> of these <u>echoes</u> are <u>processed by a computer</u> to produce a <u>video image</u> of the fetus.

Partially reflected — completely revised...

It's crazy to think that you can use sound waves to make a image — but that's the basis of <u>ultrasound scanning</u>. And it all comes down to some simple reflection and a bit of distance = speed × time.

Lenses and Magnification

This bit is about how light acts when it hits a lens. Be ready for lots of diagrams on the next few pages.

Different Lenses **Produce** Different **Kinds of** Image

Lenses form images by refracting light and changing its direction — each bit acts like a tiny prism, refracting light as it goes in and again as it goes out. There are two types of lens:

1) A converging lens is a convex lens — it bulges outwards. It causes parallel rays of light to converge (come together) at the principal focus.

2) A diverging lens is a concave lens — it caves inwards. It causes parallel rays of light to diverge (spread out).

3) The axis of a lens is a line passing through the middle of the lens.

4) The principal focus of a converging lens is where rays hitting the lens parallel to the axis all meet.

5) The principal focus of a diverging lens is the point where rays hitting the lens parallel to the axis appear to all come from — you can trace them back until they all appear to meet up at a point behind the lens.

6) There is a principal focus on each side of the lens. The distance from the centre of the lens to the principal focus is called the focal length.

Lenses can Produce Real and Virtual Images

1) A real image is where the light from an object comes together to form an image on a 'screen' — like the image formed on an eye's retina (the 'screen' at the back of an eye).

2) A virtual image is when the rays are diverging, so the light from the object appears to be coming from a completely different place.

3) When you look in a mirror you see a virtual image of your face — because the object (your face) appears to be behind the mirror.

4) You can also get a virtual image with a magnifying lens (see below).

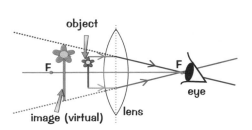

> To describe an image properly, you need to say 3 things: 1) How big it is compared to the object; 2) Whether it's upright or inverted (upside down) relative to the object; 3) Whether it's real or virtual.

Magnifying Glasses Use Converging Lenses

Magnifying glasses work by creating a magnified virtual image.

1) The object being magnified must be closer to the lens than the focal length.

2) Since the image produced is a virtual image, the light rays don't actually come from the place where the image appears to be.

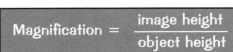

3) Remember "you can't project a virtual image onto a screen" — that's a useful phrase to use in the exam if they ask you about virtual images.

4) You can use the magnification formula to work out the magnification produced by a lens at a given distance:

$$\text{Magnification} = \frac{\text{image height}}{\text{object height}}$$

Example: A coin with diameter 14 mm is placed a certain distance behind a magnifying lens. The virtual image produced has a diameter of 35 mm. What is the magnification of the lens at this distance?

ANS: magnification = 35 ÷ 14 = <u>2.5</u>

You're virtually finished — but not really...

Remember that the proper word to describe an upside down image is inverted — you will be expected to know it.

Converging Lenses

At some point in your life, you're going to have to draw a <u>ray diagram</u> of refraction through a lens. Fun...

There are Three Rules for Refraction in a Converging Lens

1) An incident ray <u>parallel to the axis</u> refracts through the lens and passes through the <u>principal focus</u> on the other side.

2) An incident ray passing <u>through the principal focus</u> before entering the lens will refract through the lens and travel <u>parallel to the axis</u>.

3) An incident ray passing through the <u>centre</u> of the lens carries on in the <u>same direction</u>.

Lenses have a principal focus on both sides.

The <u>neat thing</u> about these rules is that they allow you to draw ray diagrams <u>without</u> bending the rays as they go into the lens <u>and</u> as they leave the lens. You can draw the diagrams as if each ray only changes direction <u>once</u>, in the <u>middle of the lens</u>.

Use a Ray Diagram to Find the Position and Size of an Image

1) Draw a line from the <u>top</u> of the object to the lens that is <u>parallel</u> to the <u>axis</u> of the lens.

2) Draw a second line from the <u>top</u> of the object to the <u>middle</u> of the lens.

3) The incident ray that's <u>parallel</u> to the axis is <u>refracted</u> through the <u>principal focus</u> (F). Draw a line representing the <u>refracted ray</u> passing through the <u>principal focus</u> of the lens.

4) The ray passing through the <u>middle</u> of the lens doesn't bend, so continue the line <u>through the lens</u> and <u>out the other side</u>.

5) Where the lines <u>meet</u> is the <u>top of the image</u>.

6) And once you've done all that, <u>do it all again</u> for the bottom of the object.

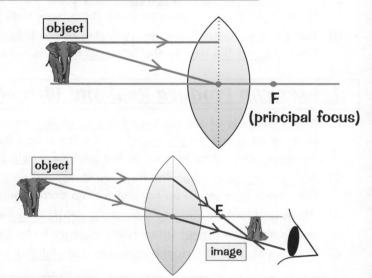

If you <u>really</u> want to draw a <u>third incident ray</u> passing through the <u>principal focus</u> on the way to the lens, you can (refract it so that it goes <u>parallel to the axis</u>). In the <u>exam</u>, you can get away with <u>two rays</u>, so no need to bother with three.

The Position of the Object Affects the Image

Remember, converging lenses can also be called convex lenses.

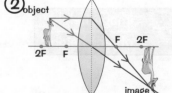
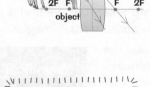

See p.47 for more on virtual and real images.

	①	②	③
Position of object	At 2F	Between F and 2F	Nearer than F
Real or virtual image?	real	real	virtual
Image orientation	inverted	inverted	right way up
Image size	same as object	bigger than object	bigger than object
Image position	at 2F	beyond 2F	same side of the lens as the object

Some things look better from a distance...

I know, I know, that table isn't very nice, but that's the information you're going to <u>need to know</u> about the joys of converging lenses and images, so make sure you learn it. When it comes to figuring out if the image is real or virtual, just remember — if it can be projected on a screen it is real. If it can't it's virtual. Sorted.

Diverging Lenses

Another day, another ray... diagram. This time for diverging lenses. There's only one way to learn how to do these really — and that's practice, practice and more practice. Good luck!

There are Three Rules for Refraction in a Diverging Lens

1) An incident ray parallel to the axis refracts through the lens, and travels in line with the principal focus (so it appears to have come from the principal focus).

2) An incident ray passing towards the principal focus refracts through the lens and travels parallel to the axis.

3) An incident ray passing through the centre of the lens carries on in the same direction.

As with the rules for a converging lens — these rules allow you to draw the diagrams as if each ray only changes direction once, in the middle of the lens. Whoop whoop for speedy shortcuts.

Draw a Ray Diagram for an Image Through a Diverging Lens

1) Pick a point on the top of the object. Draw a ray going from the object to the lens parallel to the axis of the lens.

2) Draw another ray from the top of the object going right through the middle of the lens.

3) The incident ray that's parallel to the axis is refracted so it appears to have come from the principal focus. Draw a ray from the principal focus. Make it dotted before it reaches the lens.

4) The ray passing through the middle of the lens doesn't bend.

5) Mark where the refracted rays meet. That's the top of the image.

6) Repeat the process for a point on the bottom of the object. When the bottom of the object is on the axis, the bottom of the image is also on the axis.

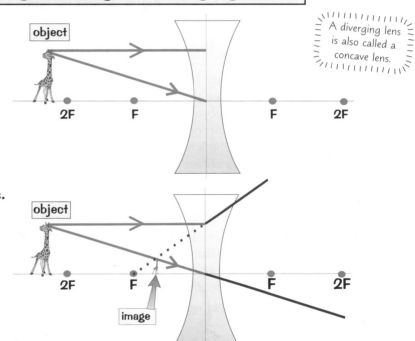

A diverging lens is also called a concave lens.

Again, if you really want to draw a third incident ray in the direction of the principal focus on the far side of the lens, you can. Remember to refract it so that it goes parallel to the axis. In the exam, you can get away with two rays. Choose whichever two are easiest to draw — don't try to draw a ray that won't actually pass through the lens.

The Image is Always Virtual

1) A diverging lens always produces a virtual image (see p. 47).

2) The image is right way up, smaller than the object and on the same side of the lens as the object — no matter where the object is.

Virtual giraffes — a bit on the small side...

The tricky part here is remembering that the diverging ray acts as if it's come from the principal focus on the same side as the image — get your head round that and your diverging lens ray diagrams will be fabulous. Always draw ray diagrams with a ruler — wiggly lines don't help one bit when you're trying to figure out where the image is.

Power and the Lens Equation

You wanna know just how <u>powerful</u> a <u>lens</u> is? Well it's all explained below...

A Powerful Lens has a Short Focal Length

1) Focal length is related to <u>power</u>. The more <u>powerful</u> the lens, the more <u>strongly</u> it converges rays of light, so the <u>shorter the focal length</u>.

$$\text{Power} = \frac{1}{\text{focal length (m)}} \quad (P = \tfrac{1}{f})$$
(D or m⁻¹)

E.g. for a lens with f = 0.2 m, power = 1 ÷ 0.2 = 5 D
(D stands for dioptres)

2) The <u>power</u> of a <u>converging lens</u> is always <u>positive</u>. The <u>power</u> of a <u>diverging lens</u> is always <u>negative</u>.

3) To make a <u>more powerful</u> lens with a smaller focal length from a certain material, e.g. glass, you just have to make it with more <u>strongly curved surfaces</u>.

4) <u>Power</u> and <u>focal length</u> also depend on the <u>refractive index</u> of the lens <u>material</u>. The <u>greater</u> the refractive index, the <u>more powerful</u> the lens (so the focal length is shorter). So, for a lens with a <u>fixed power and focal length</u>, using a material with a <u>greater</u> refractive index means that the lens can be made <u>flatter</u> (handy for making <u>glasses</u>).

The Lens Equation Works for Converging Lenses

1) Converging lenses can form <u>both</u> <u>real</u> and <u>virtual images</u> (see p. 47) depending on where the object is. If the object is further than <u>one</u> <u>focal length</u> away from the lens, the image is <u>real</u>. If the object's closer, the image is <u>virtual</u>.

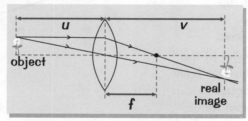 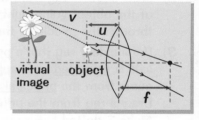

2) The distance from the centre of the lens to the object, u, is the <u>object distance</u>. v is the <u>image distance</u> — the distance between the lens and the image, and f is the <u>focal length</u>. All units are metres (m).

3) The relationship between the <u>position of the object</u>, the <u>position of the image</u> and the <u>focal length</u> relative to the lens is described by the <u>lens equation</u>.

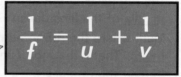

$$\frac{1}{f} = \frac{1}{u} + \frac{1}{v}$$

4) v is <u>positive</u> if the image is <u>real</u>, and <u>negative</u> if the image is <u>virtual</u>.

<u>EXAMPLE:</u> An egg sits <u>3 cm</u> from a convex lens with a <u>focal length 1 cm</u>. Describe the image of the egg the lens will produce. How far is the image from the lens?

<u>ANSWER:</u> $u = 0.03$ m, $f = 0.01$ m, and the lens equation states: $\frac{1}{f} = \frac{1}{u} + \frac{1}{v}$

Rearranging this equation, you can find v, using: $v = \dfrac{1}{\frac{1}{f} - \frac{1}{u}}$

$$v = \frac{1}{\frac{1}{0.01} - \frac{1}{0.03}} = \frac{1}{(100 - 33.3)} = \frac{1}{66.7} = 0.015 \text{ m} = 1.5 \text{ cm}$$

$v = $ <u>1.5 cm</u> which means that the image is <u>real</u> (because v is positive) inverted, and <u>1.5 cm</u> from the lens.

With great curves comes great power...

The lens equation relates the <u>focal length</u> of a lens to the <u>position</u> of the <u>image</u> it creates <u>relative</u> to the <u>object</u>. When it comes to exam time, make sure you're comfortable with that equation — it's not the easiest.

The Eye

The eye is an absolute <u>marvel of evolution</u> — the way all the different parts work together to form an image and transport it to your brain is quite astonishing... Well, I like it anyway.

You Need to Know the Basic Structure of the Eye

1) The <u>cornea</u> is a transparent 'window' with a <u>convex shape</u>, and a <u>high refractive index</u>. The cornea does most of the eye's <u>focusing</u>.

2) The <u>iris</u> is the <u>coloured</u> part of the eye. It's made up of muscles that <u>control</u> the size of the <u>pupil</u> — the hole in the middle of the iris. This <u>controls</u> the <u>intensity of light</u> entering the eye.

3) The <u>lens</u> changes shape to focus light from objects at <u>varying distances</u>. It's connected to the <u>ciliary muscles</u> by the <u>suspensory ligaments</u> and when the ciliary muscles <u>contract</u>, tension is released and the lens takes on a <u>fat</u>, more <u>spherical shape</u>. When they relax, the <u>suspensory ligaments</u> pull the lens into a thinner, <u>flatter shape</u>.

4) Images are formed on the <u>retina</u>, which is covered in <u>light-sensitive cells</u>. These cells <u>detect light</u> and send signals to the <u>brain</u> to be interpreted.

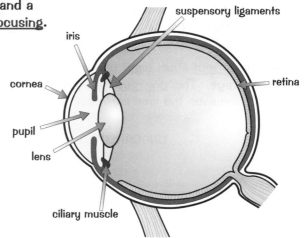

The Eye can Focus on Objects Between the Near and Far Points

1) The <u>far point</u> is the <u>furthest distance</u> that the eye can focus <u>comfortably</u>. For normally-sighted people, that's <u>infinity</u>.

2) The <u>near point</u> is the <u>closest distance</u> that the eye can focus on. For adults, the near point is approximately <u>25 cm</u>.

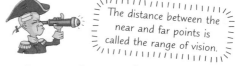

The distance between the near and far points is called the range of vision.

3) As the eye focuses on <u>closer objects</u>, its <u>power increases</u> — the lens <u>changes shape</u> and the <u>focal length decreases</u>. But the distance between the lens and the image <u>stays the same</u>.

A Camera Forms Images in a Similar Way to the Eye

When you take a photograph of a flower, light from the object (flower) travels to the camera and is refracted by the lens, forming an image on the film.

1) The image on the film is a <u>real image</u> — it is <u>smaller</u> than the object and <u>inverted</u>.

2) The <u>same</u> thing happens in our <u>eye</u> — a <u>real, inverted image</u> forms on the <u>retina</u>. Our very clever brains <u>flip</u> the image so that we see it right way up.

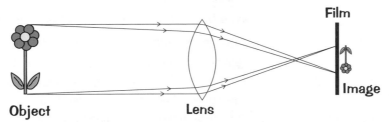

Object   Lens

Film

Image

3) In the <u>eye</u>, the image is brought into focus by <u>changing the shape</u> of the lens. In a <u>camera</u>, the image is focused by <u>moving the lens</u> closer to, or further from, the object.

4) The <u>film</u> in a camera, or the <u>CCD</u> image sensor in a digital camera, are the <u>equivalent</u> of the <u>retina</u> in the eye — they all detect the light focused on them and record it.

Eyes eyes baby...

The <u>light-sensitive cells</u> in the retina at the back of the eye send signals to the brain depending on the <u>amount</u> and <u>colour</u> of the light they've been exposed to. Then your <u>grey matter</u> works out all the different signals, forms an image, puts the image the right way up and figures out what it is. See, I told you it was nifty.

Correcting Vision

Sometimes things go a little awry in the eye department — and that's when physics steps in to save the day.

Short Sight _is Corrected with_ Diverging Lenses

1) Short-sighted people can't focus on <u>distant objects</u> — their <u>far point is closer than infinity</u> (see p.51).

2) Short sight is caused by the <u>eyeball being too long</u>, or by the <u>cornea</u> and <u>lens system</u> being too <u>powerful</u> — this means the eye lens <u>can't produce</u> a focused image on the <u>retina</u> where it is supposed to.

3) Images of distant objects are brought into focus <u>in front of</u> the retina instead, so they're blurry.

4) To <u>correct</u> short sight you need to put a <u>diverging lens</u> (with a <u>negative</u> power, see p.50) in front of the eye. This <u>diverges</u> light <u>before</u> it enters the eye, so it <u>appears</u> to have <u>come from</u> the <u>real far point</u>. This means the lens can then focus it on the <u>retina</u> producing a <u>sharp</u>, <u>clear image</u>.

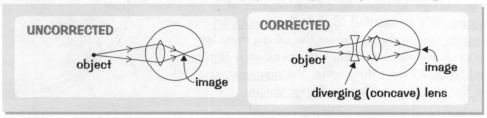

UNCORRECTED

object

image

CORRECTED

object

image

diverging (concave) lens

Long Sight _is Corrected with_ Converging Lenses

Many young children are long -sighted — their lenses grow quicker than their eyeballs.

1) Long-sighted people can't focus clearly on <u>near objects</u> — their <u>near point</u> is <u>further away than normal</u> (25 cm or more, see p.51).

2) Long sight happens when the <u>cornea and lens are too weak</u> or the <u>eyeball is too short</u>.

3) This means that images of <u>near objects</u> are brought into focus <u>behind the retina</u>, so they're blurry.

4) To correct long sight a <u>converging</u> lens (with a <u>positive</u> power, see p.50) can be put in front of the eye. The light is refracted and starts to <u>converge before</u> it enters the eye, so it <u>appears</u> to have <u>come from</u> the <u>real near point</u>. The image can now be focused on the <u>retina</u>, nice and <u>sharp</u>, where it belongs.

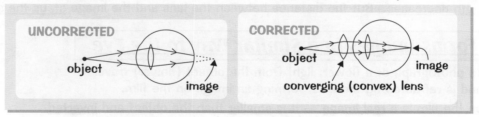

UNCORRECTED

object

image

CORRECTED

object

image

converging (convex) lens

Lasers _are Used to_ Surgically Correct Eye Problems

A laser is an <u>narrow, intense beam</u> of <u>light</u>. The light waves that come from a laser all have the same <u>wavelength</u>.

1) Lasers can be used in surgery to <u>cut through body tissue</u>, instead of using a scalpel.

2) Lasers <u>cauterise</u> (burn and seal shut) small <u>blood vessels</u> as they cut through the tissue This <u>reduces</u> the amount of <u>blood</u> the patient loses and helps to protect against <u>infection</u>.

3) Lasers are used to treat <u>skin conditions</u> such as <u>acne scars</u>. Lasers can be used to <u>burn off</u> the top layers of <u>scarred skin</u> revealing the less-scarred lower layers.

4) One of the most common types of laser surgery is <u>eye surgery</u>. A laser can be used to <u>vaporise</u> some of the cornea to change its <u>shape</u> — which changes its <u>focusing ability</u>. This can <u>increase</u> or <u>decrease</u> the <u>power</u> of the cornea so that the eye can focus images properly on the <u>retina</u>.

LASER

Wear glasses — they give you specs appeal...

The light from a laser can be let out in <u>pulses</u> for even more <u>control</u> during delicate eye surgery. The surgeon can precisely control how much tissue the laser takes off by using the pulses of light to do only a little bit at a time.

The Doppler Effect and Red-Shift

OK. Let's not kid ourselves — this is a pretty <u>daunting</u> topic. How the universe started is obviously open to debate, but physicists have got some <u>neat ideas</u> based on their observations of the <u>stars</u>. How romantic...

The <u>Universe</u> **Seems to be** <u>Expanding</u>

As big as the universe already is, it looks like it's getting even bigger.
All its <u>galaxies</u> seem to be moving away from each other. There's good evidence for this...

1) Light **from** Other Galaxies **is** Red-shifted

1) Different chemical elements <u>absorb</u> different <u>frequencies</u> (see p.34) of light.

2) Each element produces a <u>specific pattern</u> of <u>dark lines</u> at the frequencies that it <u>absorbs</u> in the visible spectrum.

3) When we look at <u>light from distant galaxies</u> we see the <u>same patterns</u> but at <u>slightly lower frequencies</u> than they should be. There's an <u>observed</u> <u>increase in the wavelength</u> of light coming from the galaxies and the patterns have been shifted towards the <u>red end</u> of the spectrum. This is called <u>red-shift</u>.

4) It's the same effect as the vrrroomm from a racing car — the engine sounds <u>lower-pitched</u> when the car's gone past you and is <u>moving away</u> from you. This is called the Doppler effect.

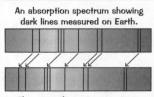

An absorption spectrum showing dark lines measured on Earth.

The same absorption spectrum measured from light from a distant galaxy. The dark lines in this spectrum are red-shifted.

The <u>Doppler Effect</u>

1) When something that emits waves moves <u>towards</u> you or <u>away</u> from you, the <u>wavelengths</u> and <u>frequencies</u> of the waves seem <u>different</u> — compared to when the source of the waves is <u>stationary</u>.

2) The <u>frequency</u> of a source moving <u>towards</u> you will seem <u>higher</u> and its <u>wavelength</u> will seem <u>shorter</u>.

3) The <u>frequency</u> of a source moving <u>away</u> from you will seem <u>lower</u> and its <u>wavelength</u> will seem <u>longer</u>.

4) The Doppler effect happens to both <u>longitudinal</u> waves (e.g. sound) and <u>transverse</u> waves (e.g. light and microwaves).

① The sound waves from a stationary car are equally spaced, like this

② But for a moving car, the wavelengths seem longer here... ...than here

③ So the frequency of the sound waves <u>seems</u> to be <u>lower</u> if the car is moving <u>away</u> from you.

2) The <u>Further Away</u> a Galaxy is, the <u>Greater</u> the <u>Red-shift</u>

1) <u>Measurements</u> of the red-shift suggest that <u>all the galaxies</u> are <u>moving away from us</u> very quickly — and it's the <u>same result</u> whichever direction you look in.

2) <u>More distant</u> galaxies have <u>greater</u> red-shifts than nearer ones — they show a <u>bigger</u> observed <u>increase in wavelength</u>.

3) This means that more distant galaxies are <u>moving away</u> from us <u>faster</u> than nearer ones.

4) This provides <u>evidence</u> that the whole <u>universe</u> is <u>expanding from</u> a very <u>small initial point</u> — the Big Bang theory (see next page).

<u>If a tree falls down in the forest and you're driving away from it...</u>

Listen out for the Doppler effect next time you hear a fast <u>motorbike</u> or a police <u>siren</u> — you should be able to work out if it's <u>coming towards</u> you or <u>speeding away</u>. You can also hear the noise in <u>cartoons</u> when someone falls off a cliff and it plays that classic <u>whistling</u> noise that gets lower, showing them accelerating away from you.

The Big Bang

Once upon a time there was a really Big Bang — that's the most convincing theory we've got.

It All Started Off with a Very Big Bang (Probably)

Right now, distant galaxies are moving away from us — the further away a galaxy is from the us, the faster they're moving away. But something must have got them going. That 'something' was probably a big explosion — so they called it the Big Bang...

1) According to this theory, all the matter and energy in the universe must have been compressed into a very small space. Then it exploded from that initial single 'point' and started expanding.

2) The expansion is still going on. We can use the current rate of expansion of the universe to estimate its age. Our best guess is that the Big Bang happened about 14 billion years ago.

3) The Big Bang isn't the only game in town. The 'Steady State' theory says that the universe has always existed as it is now, and it always will do. It's based on the idea that the universe appears pretty much the same everywhere. This theory explains the apparent expansion by suggesting that matter is being created in the spaces as the universe expands. But there are some big problems with this theory.

4) The discovery of the cosmic microwave background radiation (CMBR) some years later was strong evidence that the Big Bang was the more likely explanation of the two.

There's a Uniform Microwave Radiation from All Directions

1) Scientists have detected low frequency electromagnetic radiation coming from all parts of the universe.

2) This radiation is largely in the microwave part of the EM spectrum (see p.40). It's known as the cosmic microwave background radiation (CMBR).

3) The Big Bang theory is the only theory that can explain the CMBR.

4) Just after the Big Bang while the universe was still extremely hot, everything in the universe emitted very high frequency radiation. As the universe expanded it has cooled, and this radiation has dropped in frequency and is now seen as microwave radiation.

The Big Bang Theory Has Its Limitations

1) Today nearly all astronomers agree there was a Big Bang. However, there are some who still believe in the Steady State theory. Some of these say the evidence just points that way. Others maybe don't want to change their mind — that would mean admitting they were wrong in the first place.

2) The Big Bang theory isn't perfect. As it stands, it's not the whole explanation of the universe — there are observations that the theory can't yet explain. E.g. for complicated reasons that you don't need to know, the Big Bang theory predicts that the universe's expansion should be slowing down — but as far as we can tell it's actually speeding up.

3) The Big Bang explains the universe's expansion well, but it isn't an explanation for what actually caused the explosion in the first place, or what the conditions were like before the explosion (or if there was a 'before').

4) It seems most likely the Big Bang theory will be adapted in some way to account for its weaknesses rather than just dumped — it explains so much so well that scientists will need a lot of persuading to drop it altogether.

Time and space — it's funny old stuff isn't it...

Proving a scientific theory is impossible. If enough evidence points a certain way, then a theory can look pretty convincing. But that doesn't prove it's a fact — new evidence may change people's minds.

Revision Summary for Section Two

That was a whopper of a section. But now it's business time — another chance for you to see which bits went in and which bits you need to have another read over.

1) Draw a diagram to illustrate wavelength and amplitude.
2) What is the difference between transverse and longitudinal waves? Give two examples of each.
3)* Find the speed of a wave with frequency 50 kHz and wavelength 0.3 cm.
4) a) Sketch a diagram of a ray of light being reflected in a mirror.
   b) Label the normal and the angles of incidence and reflection.
5) Draw a diagram showing a wave diffracting through a gap.
6) What size should the gap be in order to maximise diffraction?
   a) much larger than the wavelength   b) the same size as the wavelength   c) a bit bigger than the wavelength.
7) What happens when two identical waves meet at a point?
8) Why does light bend as it moves between air and water?
9) What do we mean by the refractive index of a material?
10)* A beam of light travels from air into a block of clear plastic. The angle of incidence is 12° and the angle of refraction is 8°. What is the refractive index of the plastic block?
11) What is total internal reflection?
12) Describe how total internal reflection is used in optical fibres.
13)* What is the critical angle of a beam of light hitting the boundary going from glass to air? The refractive index of glass is 1.52.
14) Sketch the EM spectrum with all its details. Put the lowest frequency waves on the left.
15) What is the main use of radio waves?
16) What type of wave do television remotes usually use?
17) Which two types of EM wave are commonly used to send signals along optical fibres?
18) Give one use of UV light.
19) Describe two common uses of gamma rays.
20) Which is generally more hazardous — low frequency or high frequency EM radiation?
21) Describe the harmful effects on the human body that can be caused by microwaves, infrared, UV and gamma rays.
22) Describe how X-rays can be used to treat cancer.
23) What precautions can radiographers take to minimise their radiation dose?
24) Why can't sound travel in space?
25) What is ultrasound?
26)* Ultrasound travels through fat at a velocity of 1000 m/s. A pulse of ultrasound is sent into a person and is partially reflected off a layer of fat and a layer of muscle. The time between two reflected pulses of ultrasound is 0.00004 s. How thick is the layer of fat?
27) Describe the refraction of light by: a) a converging lens, b) a diverging lens.
28)* A sticker is 3.0 cm long. When the sticker is placed a certain distance behind a magnifying glass, a virtual image is produced with a length of 6.0 cm. Work out the magnification of this lens at this distance.
29) Describe the characteristics of an image formed from light from an object nearer to a converging lens than its principal focus, F.
30) Describe the image produced by a diverging lens.
31)* Find the power of a lens with a focal length of 0.25 m.
32) Draw a simple sketch of the eye and label the following:
   a) cornea,   b) iris,   c) pupil,   d) lens,   e) retina,   f) ciliary muscles.
33) What type of lens could be used to correct: a) short sight,   b) long sight?
34) If a wave source is moving towards you, will the observed frequency of its waves be higher or lower than their actual frequency?
35) Describe the 'Big Bang' theory for the origin of the universe. What evidence is there for this theory?

* Answers on p. 100.

Kinetic Theory and Changes of State

Kinetic theory sounds complicated but it's actually pretty simple. It just describes how particles <u>move</u> in <u>solids</u>, <u>liquids</u> and <u>gases</u>. The <u>energy</u> an object (or particle) has because of its <u>movement</u> is called its <u>kinetic energy</u>.

Kinetic Theory *Can Explain the Three States of Matter*

The <u>three states of matter</u> are <u>solid</u> (e.g. ice), <u>liquid</u> (e.g. water) and <u>gas</u> (e.g. water vapour). The <u>particles</u> of a particular substance in each state are <u>the same</u> — only the <u>arrangement</u> and <u>energy</u> of the particles are <u>different</u>.

SOLIDS — <u>strong forces</u> of attraction hold the particles <u>close together</u> in a <u>fixed</u>, <u>regular</u> arrangement. The particles don't have much <u>energy</u> so they <u>can</u> only <u>vibrate</u> about their <u>fixed</u> positions.

LIQUIDS — there are <u>weaker forces</u> of attraction between the particles. The particles are <u>close together</u>, but can <u>move past each other</u>, and form <u>irregular</u> arrangements. They have <u>more energy</u> than the particles in a <u>solid</u> — they move in <u>random directions</u> at <u>low speeds</u>.

GASES — There are <u>almost no</u> forces of attraction between the particles. The particles have <u>more energy</u> than those in <u>liquids</u> and <u>solids</u> — they are <u>free to move</u>, and travel in <u>random directions</u> and at <u>high speeds</u>.

When you <u>heat</u> a substance, you give its particles <u>more kinetic energy</u> (E_K) — they <u>vibrate</u> or <u>move faster</u>. This is what eventually causes <u>solids</u> to <u>melt</u> and <u>liquids</u> to <u>boil</u>.

You Need to *Put In Energy to Break Intermolecular Bonds*

1) When you heat a liquid, the <u>heat energy</u> makes the <u>particles move faster</u>. Eventually, when enough of the particles have enough energy to overcome their attraction to each other, big bubbles of <u>gas</u> form in the liquid — this is <u>boiling</u>.

2) It's similar when you heat a solid. <u>Heat energy</u> makes the <u>particles vibrate faster</u> until eventually the forces between them are overcome and the particles start to move around — this is <u>melting</u>.

3) The <u>melting point</u> of a solid and the <u>boiling point</u> of a liquid are <u>affected</u> by <u>impurities</u> — other things in the substance that <u>aren't molecules</u> of that substance. For example, the boiling point of <u>pure water</u> is 100 °C, but if you <u>add salt</u> (an impurity) then its boiling point will <u>increase</u> (depending on <u>how much</u> salt you add).

4) When a substance is <u>melting</u> or <u>boiling</u>, you're still putting in <u>energy</u>, but the energy's used for <u>breaking intermolecular bonds</u> rather than raising the temperature. There are <u>flat spots</u> on the heating graph where <u>latent heat energy</u> is being <u>transferred</u>, but not being used to change the temperature.

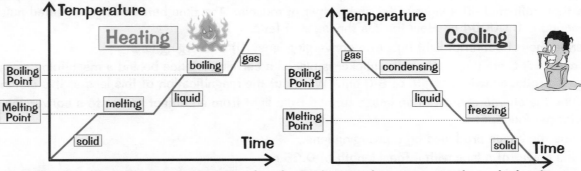

5) When a substance is <u>condensing</u> or <u>freezing</u>, bonds are <u>forming</u> between particles, which <u>releases</u> energy. This means the <u>temperature doesn't go down</u> until all the substance has turned to liquid (condensing) or a solid (freezing). Again, the <u>flat parts</u> of the graphs show these times when energy is being transferred.

Breaking Bonds — Blofeld never quite manages it...

Melting a solid or boiling a liquid means you've got to <u>break bonds</u> between particles. That takes energy. Incidentally, this is how <u>sweating</u> cools you down — your body heat is used to change liquid sweat into gas. What a brilliant fact you can use to impress your friends. My work here is done.

Specific Heat Capacity

Specific heat capacity is one of those topics that puts people off just because it has a weird name. If you can get over that, it's actually not too bad — it sounds a lot harder than it is. Go on. Give it a second chance.

Specific Heat Capacity Tells You How Much Energy Stuff Can Store

1) It takes more heat energy to increase the temperature of some materials than others.

2) E.g. you need 4200 J to warm 1 kg of water by 1 °C, but only 139 J to warm 1 kg of mercury by 1 °C.

3) Materials which need to gain lots of energy to warm up also release loads of energy when they cool down again. They can 'store' a lot of heat.

4) The measure of how much energy a substance can store is called its specific heat capacity.

5) Specific heat capacity is the amount of energy needed to raise the temperature of 1 kg of a substance by 1 °C.

6) Water has a specific heat capacity of 4200 J/kg°C.

There's a Handy Formula for Specific Heat Capacity

You'll have to do calculations involving specific heat capacity. This is the equation to learn:

Energy transferred (J) → $$E = m \times c \times \theta$$ ← Temperature change (°C)

Mass (kg) — Specific heat capacity (J/kg°C)

> **EXAMPLE:** How much energy is needed to heat 2 kg of water from 10 °C to 100 °C?
>
> **ANSWER:** $E = m \times c \times \theta$, where m = 2 kg, c = 4200 J/kg°C and θ = 100 − 10 = 90 °C.
>
> Energy needed = 2 × 4200 × 90 = 756 000 J

If you're not working out the energy, you'll have to rearrange the equation, so this formula triangle will come in dead handy.

You cover up the thing you're trying to find. The parts of the formula you can still see are what it's equal to.

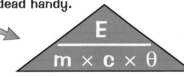

$$\frac{E}{m \times c \times \theta}$$

> **EXAMPLE:** An empty 200 g aluminium kettle cools down from 115 °C to 10 °C, losing 19 068 J of heat energy.
> What is the specific heat capacity of aluminium?
>
> **ANSWER:** You need to convert grams to kilograms first, so 200 g = 0.2 kg.
> Then rearrange the equation using the triangle above:
>
> $$SHC = \frac{Energy}{Mass \times Temp\ Ch} = \frac{19\ 068}{0.2 \times 105} = 908\ J/kg°C$$

I've just eaten five sausages — I have a high specific meat capacity...

I'm sure you'll agree that this isn't the most exciting part of physics — it's not about stars, crashing cars or even using springs — but it is likely to come up in your exams. Sadly you just have to knuckle down and get that formula triangle learnt — then you'll be well on the way to breezing through any question on this in the exam.

Specific Latent Heat

If you heat up a pan of water on the stove, the water never gets any hotter than 100 °C. You can <u>carry on heating it up</u>, but the <u>temperature won't rise</u>. How come, you say? It's all to do with <u>latent heat</u>...

Specific Latent Heat is the Energy Needed to Change State

1) The <u>specific latent heat</u> (SLH) of a substance is the <u>amount of energy</u> needed to <u>change 1 kg</u> of it from <u>one state to another</u> <u>without changing</u> its <u>temperature</u>.

2) Specific latent heat is <u>different</u> for <u>different materials</u>, and it's different for <u>boiling</u> (<u>vaporisation</u>) and <u>melting</u> (<u>fusion</u>).

SLH of Vaporisation is the Energy Needed to Boil Something

1) The <u>specific latent heat of vaporisation</u> (boiling) is the <u>amount of energy</u> needed to change <u>1 kg</u> of material <u>from liquid to vapour</u> (gas) <u>without changing its temperature</u> (i.e. the material's got to be at its boiling temperature already).

2) You don't have to remember what all the numbers are, though. Phew. There's a <u>formula</u> to help you with all the <u>calculations</u>. And here it is:

> Energy = Mass × Specific Latent Heat of Vaporisation (L$_V$)

EXAMPLE: The specific latent heat of vaporisation for water (boiling) is 2 260 000 J/kg. How much energy is needed to completely boil 1.25 kg of water at 100 °C?

ANSWER: E = m × L$_V$ = 1.25 × 2 260 000 = <u>2 825 000 J</u>

SLH of Fusion is the Energy Needed to Melt Something

1) The <u>specific latent heat of fusion</u> is the <u>amount of energy</u> needed to change <u>1 kg</u> of material <u>from a solid to a liquid</u> <u>without changing its temperature</u> (i.e. the material's got to be at its melting temperature already).

2) Here's another <u>formula</u> to help you with all the <u>calculations</u> — the cleverest among you will notice it's no different to the one above, just L$_V$ has been replaced with L$_F$. Cunning...

> Energy = Mass × Specific Latent Heat of Fusion (L$_F$)

The mass needs to be in kg. So ÷ by 1000 to change from g to kg.

EXAMPLE: The specific latent heat of fusion for water (melting) is 334 000 J/kg. How much energy is needed to melt an ice cube of mass 7 g at 0 °C?

ANSWER: E = m × L$_F$ = 0.007 × 334 000 = <u>2338 J</u>

If you're finding the mass or the specific latent heat you'll need to divide, not multiply — just to make your life a bit easier here's the formula triangle.

$$\frac{Energy}{Mass \times L_F}$$

EXAMPLE: The specific latent heat of fusion for water (melting) is 334 000 J/kg. If 4008 J of energy is needed to melt an ice cube at 0 °C, what was the mass of the ice cube?

ANSWER: m = 4008 ÷ 334 000 = 0.012 kg = <u>12 g</u>

The specific latent heat of revision...

... the amount of energy required to turn 1 kg of revision notes into a top grade. Two scary <u>equations</u>, but they're really <u>just the same one</u> with a tiny twist — L$_V$ to L$_F$. So once you've got your head round one, you should be able to use the other one no problem. That triangle is the same for both as well. Groovy.

Heat Radiation

Heat energy tends to flow away from a hotter object to its cooler surroundings.
But then you knew that already. I would hope.

Heat Is Transferred in Three Different Ways

1) Heat energy can be transferred by radiation, conduction or convection.
2) Heat radiation is the transfer of heat energy by infrared (IR) radiation (see below).
3) Conduction and convection involve the transfer of energy by particles.
4) Conduction is the main form of heat transfer in solids (see p. 60).
5) Convection is the main form of heat transfer in liquids and gases (see p. 60).
6) Infrared radiation can be emitted by solids, liquids and gases.
7) Any object can both absorb and emit infrared radiation, whether or not conduction or convection are also taking place.
8) The bigger the temperature difference between a body and its surroundings, the faster energy is transferred by heating. Kinda makes sense.

Mwah ha ha ha ha!

Infrared Radiation — Emission of Electromagnetic Waves

1) All objects are continually emitting and absorbing infrared radiation. Infrared radiation is emitted from the surface of an object.
2) An object that's hotter than its surroundings emits more radiation than it absorbs (as it cools down). And an object that's cooler than its surroundings absorbs more radiation than it emits (as it warms up).
3) The hotter an object is, the more radiation it radiates in a given time.
4) You can feel this infrared radiation if you stand near something hot like a fire or if you put your hand just above the bonnet of a recently parked car.

(recently parked car)

(after an hour or so)

Radiation Depends an Awful Lot on Surface Colour and Texture

1) Dark, matt surfaces absorb infrared radiation falling on them much better than light, shiny surfaces, such as gloss white or silver. They also emit much more infrared radiation (at any given temperature).
2) Light, shiny surfaces reflect a lot of the infrared radiation falling on them — this means they're poor absorbers of infrared radiation. They're also poor emitters. E.g. vacuum flasks have silver inner surfaces to keep heat in or out, depending on whether it's storing hot or cold liquid.

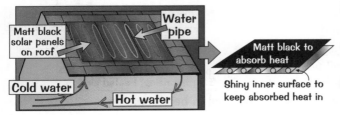

3) Solar hot water panels contain water pipes under a black surface (or black painted pipes under glass).
4) Radiation from the Sun is absorbed by the black surface to heat the water in the pipes.
5) This water can be used for washing or pumped to radiators to heat the building.

Feelin' hot hot hot...

You might be asked about an example of IR radiation that you've not come across before. As long as you remember that light, shiny surfaces reflect IR radiation and dark, matt surfaces absorb it — you should be able to figure out what's going on. If this stuff on radiation is floating your boat, you're going to love conduction...

Conduction and Convection

Conduction and convection (along with radiation) are ways in which heat energy can be transferred. They work in slightly different ways but they're both caused by the movement of heated particles. Super.

Conduction Occurs Mainly in Solids

Heat flows through solids (and to a lesser extent through liquids and gases) by conduction:

1) In a solid, the particles are held tightly together. So when one particle vibrates, it bumps into other particles nearby and quickly passes the vibrations on.

2) Particles which vibrate faster than others pass on their extra kinetic energy to neighbouring particles. These particles then vibrate faster themselves.

3) This process continues throughout the solid and gradually the extra kinetic energy (or heat) is spread all the way through the solid. This causes a rise in temperature at the other side.

> **CONDUCTION OF HEAT** is the process where vibrating particles pass on extra kinetic energy to neighbouring particles.

4) Metals conduct heat really well because some of their electrons are free to move inside the metal. Heating makes the electrons move faster and collide with other particles in the metal, transferring energy. Because the electrons move freely, this is a much faster way of transferring energy than slowly passing it between jostling neighbouring atoms.

5) Most non-metals don't have free electrons, so warm up more slowly, making them good for insulating things — that's why metals are used for saucepans, but non-metals are used for saucepan handles.

6) Liquids and gases conduct heat more slowly than solids — the particles aren't held so tightly together, which prevents them bumping into each other so often. So air is a good insulator.

Convection Occurs in Liquids and Gases

1) When you heat up a fluid (liquid or gas), the particles move faster and move further apart from each other — so the fluid expands, becoming less dense.

2) The warmer, less dense fluid rises above its colder, denser surroundings, like a hot air balloon does.

3) As the warm fluid rises, cooler fluid takes its place. As this process continues, you actually end up with a circulation of fluid (convection currents). This is how immersion heaters work.

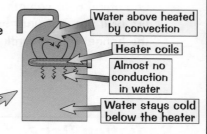

Water above heated by convection
Heater coils
Almost no conduction in water
Water stays cold below the heater

> **CONVECTION** occurs when the more energetic particles move from the hotter region to the cooler region — and take their heat energy with them.

4) Radiators in the home rely on convection to make the warm air circulate round the room.

5) Convection can't happen in solids because the particles can't move — they just vibrate on the spot.

6) To reduce convection, you need to stop the fluid moving. Clothes, blankets and cavity wall foam insulation all work by trapping pockets of air. The air can't move so the heat has to conduct very slowly through the pockets of air, as well as the material in between.

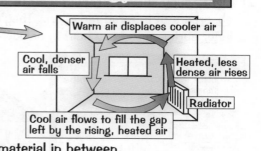

Warm air displaces cooler air
Cool, denser air falls
Heated, less dense air rises
Radiator
Cool air flows to fill the gap left by the rising, heated air

And the good old garden spade is a great example...

If a garden spade is left outside in cold weather, the metal bit will always feel colder than the wooden handle. But it isn't colder — it just conducts heat away from your hand quicker. The opposite is true if the spade is left out in the sunshine — it'll feel hotter because it conducts heat into your hand quicker.

Condensation and Evaporation

Energy can be transferred by condensation and evaporation too. Yey — it's party-cle time...

Condensation is When Gas Turns to Liquid

1) When a gas cools, the particles in the gas slow down and lose kinetic energy. The attractive forces between the particles pull them closer together.

2) If the temperature gets cold enough and the gas particles get close enough together that condensation can take place, the gas becomes a liquid.

3) Water vapour in the air condenses when it comes into contact with cold surfaces e.g. drinks glasses.

4) The steam you see rising from a boiling kettle is actually invisible water vapour condensing to form tiny water droplets as it spreads into cooler air.

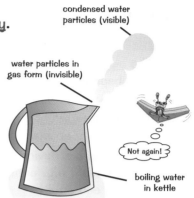

condensed water particles (visible)

water particles in gas form (invisible)

Not again!

boiling water in kettle

Evaporation is When Liquid Turns to Gas

1) Evaporation is when particles escape from a liquid.

2) Particles can evaporate from a liquid at temperatures that are much lower than the liquid's boiling point.

3) Particles near the surface of a liquid can escape and become gas particles if:

> • The particles are travelling in the right direction to escape the liquid.
> • The particles are travelling fast enough (they have enough kinetic energy) to overcome the attractive forces of the other particles in the liquid.

4) The fastest particles (with the most kinetic energy) are most likely to evaporate from the liquid — so when they do, the average speed and kinetic energy of the remaining particles decreases.

5) This decrease in average particle energy means the temperature of the remaining liquid falls — the liquid cools.

6) This cooling effect can be really useful. For example, you sweat when you exercise or get hot. As the water from the sweat on your skin evaporates, it cools you down.

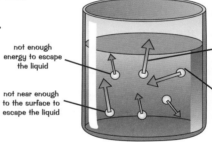

not enough energy to escape the liquid

not near enough to the surface to escape the liquid

this particle is able to escape the liquid and evaporates

moving in the wrong direction to escape the liquid

Rates of Evaporation can Vary

The RATE OF EVAPORATION will be faster if the...

• TEMPERATURE is higher — the average particle energy will be higher, so more particles will have enough energy to escape.

• DENSITY is lower — the forces between the particles will usually be weaker, so more particles will have enough energy to overcome these forces and escape the liquid.

• SURFACE AREA is larger — more particles will be near enough to the surface to escape the liquid.

• AIRFLOW over the liquid is greater — the lower the concentration of an evaporating substance in the air it's evaporating into, the higher the rate of evaporation. A greater airflow means air above the liquid is replaced more quickly, so the concentration in the air will be lower.

• HUMIDITY is lower — humidity is a measure of the amount of water vapour in the air. If this is lower, then the concentration of water particles in the air will be lower, and so the rate of evaporation will be higher. (And the cooling effect of evaporation will be greater.)

A little less condensation, a little more action...

The people who make adverts for drinks know what customers like to see — condensation on the outside of the bottle. It makes the drink look nice and cold and extra-refreshing. Mmmm. If it wasn't for condensation, you'd never be able to draw pictures on the bus window with your finger either — you've got a lot to be thankful for...

Rate of Heat Transfer and Expansion

There are loads of factors that affect the <u>rate</u> of <u>heat transfer</u>.
Different objects can lose or gain heat much <u>faster</u> than others — even in the <u>same conditions</u>. Read on...

The Rate of Heat Energy Transfer Depends on Many Things...

1) <u>Heat energy</u> is <u>radiated</u> from the <u>surface</u> of an object.

2) The <u>bigger</u> the <u>surface area</u>, the <u>more infrared waves</u> that can be <u>emitted</u> from (or absorbed by) the surface — so the <u>quicker</u> the <u>transfer of heat</u>. E.g. <u>radiators</u> have <u>large surface areas</u> to <u>maximise</u> the amount of heat they transfer.

3) This is why <u>car and motorbike engines</u> often have 'fins' — they <u>increase</u> the <u>surface area</u> so heat is radiated away quicker. So the <u>engine cools quicker</u>.

Cooling fins on engines increase surface area to speed up cooling.

4) <u>Heat sinks</u> are devices designed to transfer heat <u>away</u> from <u>objects</u> they're in <u>contact</u> with, e.g. computer components. They have <u>fins</u> and a large <u>surface area</u> so they can <u>emit heat</u> as <u>quickly</u> as possible.

5) If two objects at the <u>same</u> temperature have the same surface area but <u>different</u> volumes, the object with the <u>smaller</u> volume will cool more <u>quickly</u> — as a higher proportion of the object will be in <u>contact</u> with its surroundings.

6) Other factors, like the temperature of the <u>surroundings</u> (see p.59) and <u>type</u> of material, affect the rate too. Objects made from <u>conductors</u> transfer heat away more <u>quickly</u> than <u>insulating</u> materials, e.g. <u>plastic</u>. It also matters whether the materials in <u>contact</u> with the object are <u>insulators</u> or <u>conductors</u>. If it's in contact with a <u>conductor</u>, the heat will be conducted away <u>faster</u> than if it's in contact with an <u>insulator</u>.

Humans and Animals Have Ways of Controlling Heat Transfer Too

1) In the <u>cold</u>, the hairs on your skin 'stand up' to trap a <u>thicker</u> layer of <u>insulating air</u> around the body. This limits the amount of heat loss by <u>convection</u>. Some animals do the same using <u>fur</u>.

2) When you're <u>too warm</u>, your body diverts more <u>blood</u> to flow near the surface of your skin so that more heat can be lost by <u>radiation</u> — that's why some people go <u>pink</u> when they get hot.

3) Generally, animals in <u>warm</u> climates have <u>larger</u> ears than those in <u>cold</u> climates to help <u>control</u> heat transfer.

For example, Arctic foxes have evolved <u>small ears</u>, with a small surface area to minimise <u>heat loss</u> by <u>radiation</u> and conserve body heat.

Desert foxes on the other hand have <u>huge ears</u> with a large surface area to allow them to <u>lose heat</u> by <u>radiation</u> easily and keep cool.

Most Substances Expand When Heated

1) When substances are <u>heated</u>, their <u>particles</u> <u>gain kinetic energy</u> and they <u>move further apart</u> (even in solids). This means they <u>expand</u> and their <u>volume increases</u>.

2) <u>How much</u> they expand depends on <u>what</u> they're made of and their <u>temperature</u> change.

3) This property can be a <u>hazard</u> — structures like <u>roofs</u> and <u>bridges</u> are built with precise measurements. If the material they're made from expands in heat (and contracts when it's cold), this needs to be taken into account to make sure they don't <u>collapse or become dangerous</u> when the temperature changes.

4) Expansion in heat can also be <u>useful</u> — <u>bi-metallic strips</u> are made of <u>two different</u> types of <u>metal</u> that <u>expand at different rates</u>, joined together. This means the strip will <u>bend</u> one way when <u>heated</u> and the <u>other way</u> when <u>cooled</u>. They are used in lots of devices, including <u>thermostats</u> (temperature controllers in heating systems) — as they change shape (according to temperature) they <u>control</u> whether the <u>heating</u> switches on or off.

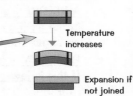

Temperature increases

Expansion if not joined

Don't call me 'Big Ears' — call me 'Large Surface Area'...

You could be asked to explain the design of items in terms of <u>energy transfer</u> — talk about what form of heat transfer is involved at any point (<u>conduction</u>, <u>convection</u>, <u>radiation</u>, <u>condensation</u> or <u>evaporation</u>) and how the item is designed to <u>increase</u> or <u>decrease</u> energy transfer in this way — it's the only way to get top marks.

Energy Transfer and Efficiency

Devices and machines (like computers or motors or me!) transfer energy from one form to another. Cool.

Energy can be Transferred But NOT Created or Destroyed

ENERGY CAN BE TRANSFERRED USEFULLY FROM ONE FORM TO ANOTHER, STORED OR DISSIPATED — BUT IT CAN NEVER BE CREATED OR DESTROYED.

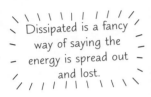
Dissipated is a fancy way of saying the energy is spread out and lost.

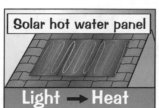
Solar hot water panel

Light → Heat

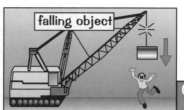
falling object

Gravitational Potential → Kinetic

You might be asked to describe the energy transfers that take place in any device — make sure you can.

But energy is only useful when it can be converted from one form to another.

Most Energy Transfers Involve Some Losses, Often as Heat

1) Useful devices are only useful because they can transform energy from one form to another.
2) In doing so, some of the useful input energy is always lost or wasted, often as heat (or sound, light, etc).
3) The less energy that is 'wasted', the more efficient the device is said to be.
4) No device is 100% efficient — the wasted heat (or other) energy is lost to the surroundings, making them warmer. This energy spreads out further and further and so becomes useless.

It's Really Simple to Calculate Efficiency...

A machine is a device that turns one type of energy into another. The efficiency of any device is defined as:

$$\text{Efficiency} = \frac{\text{Useful Energy out}}{\text{Total Energy in}} \ (\times 100\%)$$

If you don't know the energy inputs and outputs you can still calculate the machine's efficiency as long as you know the power input and output:

You can give efficiency as a decimal or you can multiply your answer by 100 to get a percentage, i.e. 0.75 or 75%.

$$\text{Efficiency} = \frac{\text{Useful Power out}}{\text{Total Power in}} \ (\times 100\%)$$

As usual, a formula triangle will come handy for rearranging the formulas:

Useful Out

Efficiency × Total In

How to Use the Formula — Nothing to It

1) You find how much energy is supplied to a machine. (The Total Energy IN.)
2) You find how much useful energy the machine delivers. (The Useful Energy OUT.)
   An exam question either tells you this directly or tells you how much it wastes as heat/sound.
3) Either way, you get those two important numbers and then just divide the smaller one by the bigger one to get a value for efficiency somewhere between 0 and 1 (or 0 and 100%). Easy.
4) The other way they might ask it is to tell you the efficiency and the input energy and ask for the energy output — so you need to be able to swap the formula round.

Don't waste your energy — turn the TV off while you revise...

And for 10 bonus points, calculate the efficiency of these machines:
TV — energy in = 220 J, light energy out = 5 J, sound energy out = 2 J, heat energy out = 213 J.
Loudspeaker — energy in = 35 J, sound energy out = 0.5 J, heat energy out = 34.5 J. Answers on p. 100.

Sankey Diagrams

This is another opportunity for a MATHS question. Fantastic. So best prepare yourself — here's what those Sankey diagrams (energy transformation diagrams) are all about...

The Thickness of the Arrow Represents the Amount of Energy

The idea of Sankey diagrams is to make it easy to see at a glance how much of the total energy in is being usefully employed compared with how much is being wasted.

The thicker the arrow, the more energy it represents — so you see a big thick arrow going in, then several smaller arrows going off it to show the different energy transformations taking place.

You can have either a little sketch or a properly detailed diagram where the width of each arrow is proportional to the number of joules it represents.

Example — TV:

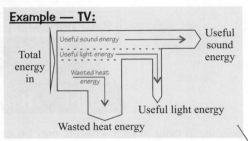

Example — Sankey Diagram for a Simple Motor:

HERE'S THE SKETCH VERSION:

Total energy in → Useful kinetic energy
Heat energy   Sound energy

You don't know the actual amounts, but you can see that most of the energy is being wasted, and that it's mostly wasted as heat.

EXAM QUESTIONS:

With sketches, they're likely to ask you to compare two different devices and say which is more efficient. You generally want to be looking for the one with the thickest useful energy arrow(s).

AND HERE'S THE DETAILED ONE:

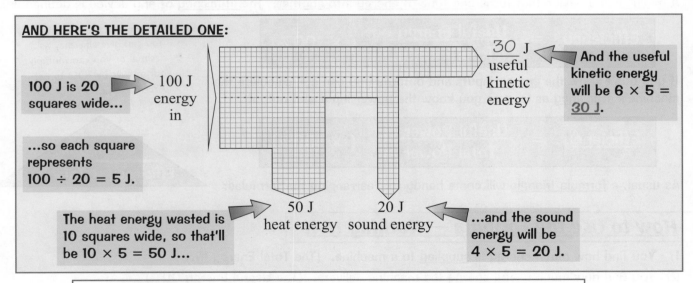

100 J is 20 squares wide...

...so each square represents
100 ÷ 20 = 5 J.

The heat energy wasted is 10 squares wide, so that'll be 10 × 5 = 50 J...

And the useful kinetic energy will be 6 × 5 = 30 J.

...and the sound energy will be 4 × 5 = 20 J.

EXAM QUESTIONS:

In an exam, the most likely question you'll get about detailed Sankey diagrams is filling in one of the numbers or calculating the efficiency. The efficiency is straightforward enough if you can work out the numbers (see p. 63).

Skankey diagrams — to represent the smelliness of your socks...

If they ask you to draw your own Sankey diagram in the exam, and don't give you the figures, a sketch is all they'll expect. Just give a rough idea of where the energy goes. E.g. a filament lamp turns most of the input energy into heat, and only a tiny proportion goes to useful light energy.

Energy Efficiency in the Home

There are lots of things you can do to a building to <u>reduce</u> the amount of <u>heat energy that escapes</u> (and so the amount of energy you <u>consume</u> and have to <u>buy</u>). Some are <u>more effective</u> than others, and some are <u>better for your pocket</u> than others. The most obvious examples are in the home, but you could apply these ideas to <u>any situation</u> where you're trying to <u>cut down</u> energy loss.

Effectiveness and Cost-effectiveness are Not the Same...

Hot Water Tank Jacket
Initial Cost: £15
Annual Saving: £30
Payback time: <u>6 months</u>

Loft Insulation
Initial Cost: £200
Annual Saving: £50
Payback time: <u>4 years</u>

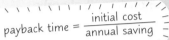

payback time = $\dfrac{\text{initial cost}}{\text{annual saving}}$

Double Glazing
Initial Cost: £3000
Annual Saving: £60
Payback time: <u>50 years</u>

Cavity Wall Insulation
Initial Cost: £500
Annual Saving: £70
Payback time: <u>7 years</u>

Draught-proofing
Initial Cost: £100
Annual Saving: £50
Payback time: <u>2 years</u>

1) The <u>most effective</u> methods of insulation are ones that give you the biggest <u>annual saving</u> (they save you the <u>most</u> money <u>each year</u> on your <u>heating bills</u>).

2) Eventually, the <u>money you've saved</u> on heating bills will <u>equal</u> the initial cost of putting in the insulation (the amount it cost to buy). The time it takes is called the <u>payback time</u>.

3) The <u>most cost-effective</u> methods tend to be the <u>cheapest</u>.

4) They are cost-effective because they have a <u>short payback time</u> — this means the money you save <u>covers</u> the amount you <u>paid</u> really <u>quickly</u>.

Know Which Types of Heat Transfer Are Involved

1) <u>CAVITY WALL INSULATION</u> — foam squirted into the gap between the bricks stops <u>convection</u> currents being set up in the gap and <u>radiation</u> across the gap. The insulating foam and the air pockets trapped in it (air is an insulator) also helps reduce heat loss by <u>conduction</u>.

2) <u>LOFT INSULATION</u> — a thick layer of fibreglass wool laid out across the whole loft floor reduces <u>conduction</u> and <u>radiation</u> into the roof space from the ceiling.

3) <u>DRAUGHT-PROOFING</u> — strips of foam and plastic around doors and windows stops warm air blowing out and draughts of cold air blowing in, i.e. they reduce heat loss due to <u>convection</u>.

4) <u>HOT WATER TANK JACKET</u> — lagging such as fibreglass wool reduces <u>conduction</u> and <u>radiation</u>.

5) <u>THICK CURTAINS</u> — big bits of cloth over the window to reduce heat loss by <u>conduction</u> and <u>radiation</u>.

U-Values Show How Effective an Insulator Is

1) <u>Heat</u> transfers <u>faster</u> through materials with <u>higher U-values</u> than through materials with low U-values.

2) So the <u>better the insulator</u> the <u>lower</u> the U-value. E.g. The U-value of a typical <u>duvet</u> is about <u>0.75 W/m²K</u>, whereas the U-value of <u>loft insulation material</u> is around <u>0.15 W/m²K</u>.

It's payback time...

And it's the same with, say, cars. Buying a more fuel-efficient car might sound like a great idea — but if it costs loads more than a clapped-out old fuel-guzzler, you might still end up out of pocket. If it's <u>cost-effectiveness</u> you're thinking about, you always have to offset initial cost against annual savings.

Revision Summary for Section Three

It's all very well reading the pages and looking at the diagrams — but you won't have a hope of remembering it for your exam if you don't understand it. Have a go at these questions to see how much has gone in so far. If you struggle with any of them, have another read through the section and give the questions another go.

1) Describe the arrangement and movement of the particles in   a) solids   b) liquids   c) gases.
2) Explain why heating a pan of boiling water doesn't increase its temperature.
3) What is specific heat capacity?
4)* It takes 5000 J to heat 50 g of a substance by 40 °C. Calculate its specific heat capacity.
5)* How much energy is needed to boil dry a pan of 500 g of water at 100 °C?
   (Specific latent heat of vaporisation of water for boiling = 2 260 000 J/kg.)
6) Describe the three ways that heat energy can be transferred.
7) True or false? An object that's cooler than its surroundings emits more radiation than it absorbs.
8) Explain why solar hot water panels have a matt black surface.
9) What is the name of the process where vibrating particles
   pass on their extra kinetic energy to neighbouring particles?
10) Which type of heat transfer can't take place in solids — convection or conduction?
11) How do the densities of liquids and gases change as you heat them?
12) Describe how the heat from heater coils is transferred throughout the water in a kettle.
   What is this process called?
13) What happens to the particles of a gas as it turns to a liquid?
14) What is the name given to the process where a gas turns to a liquid?
15) Why does evaporation have a cooling effect on a liquid?
16) The two designs of car engine shown are made from the same material.
   Which engine will transfer heat quicker? Explain why.

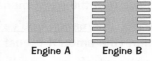
Engine A   Engine B

17) Do animals that live in hot climates tend to have large or small ears?
   Give one reason why this might be an advantage in a hot climate.
18) List the energy transformations that occur in a battery-powered toy car.
19) What is the useful type of energy delivered by a motor? In what form is energy wasted?
20)*What is the efficiency of a motor that converts 100 J of electrical energy into 70 J of useful kinetic energy?
21)* The following Sankey diagram shows how energy is converted in a catapult.

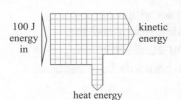
100 J energy in   kinetic energy
heat energy

a) How much energy is converted into kinetic energy?
b) How much energy is wasted?
c) What is the efficiency of the catapult?

22)*If it costs £4000 to double glaze your house and the double glazing saves you
   £100 on energy bills every year, calculate the payback time for double glazing.
23) Name five ways of improving energy efficiency in the home. Explain how each improvement
   reduces the amount of heat lost from a house.
24) What can you tell from a material's U-value?
25) Would you expect copper or cotton wool to have a higher U-value?

* Answers on p. 100.

Current and Potential Difference

Isn't <u>electricity</u> great. Mind you it's pretty bad news if the <u>words</u> don't mean anything to you...
Hey, I know — learn them now!

1) Current is a <u>flow</u> of electric charge round a circuit. Unit: ampere, A.
Electrical charges can <u>move easily</u> through some
materials. These materials are called <u>conductors</u>,
e.g. <u>metals</u> are <u>good</u> conductors. Current will <u>only</u>
<u>flow</u> through a component if there is a <u>potential</u>
<u>difference</u> across that component.

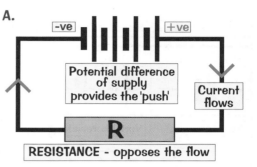

2) Potential Difference is the <u>driving force</u> that pushes the current
round. It's also called <u>voltage</u>. Unit: volt, V.

3) Resistance is anything in the circuit which <u>slows the flow down</u>.
Unit: ohm, Ω.

> The <u>greater the resistance</u> of a component,
> the <u>smaller the current</u> that flows
> (for a given potential difference across the component).

Total Charge Through a Circuit Depends on Current and Time

1) <u>The size of the electric current</u> is the <u>rate of flow</u> of <u>electric charge</u>.
When <u>current</u> (I) flows past a point in a circuit for a length of <u>time</u> (t)
then the <u>charge</u> (Q) that has passed is given by this formula:

2) <u>Current</u> is measured in <u>amperes</u> (A),
<u>charge</u> is measured in <u>coulombs</u> (C),
<u>time</u> is measured in <u>seconds</u> (s).

$$\text{Current} = \frac{\text{Charge}}{\text{Time}}$$

$$I = \frac{Q}{t}$$

3) <u>More charge</u> passes around the
circuit when a <u>bigger current</u> flows.

> <u>EXAMPLE</u>: A battery charger passes a current of 2.5 A through a cell over
> a period of 4 hours. How much charge does the charger
> transfer to the cell altogether?
>
> <u>ANSWER</u>: Q = I × t = 2.5 × (4 × 60 × 60) = 36 000 C (36 kC).

Potential Difference (P. D.) is the Energy Transferred Per Unit Charge

1) The potential difference (or <u>voltage</u>) is the <u>energy transferred</u> (the work done, measured in joules, J)
<u>per coulomb of charge</u> that passes between <u>two points</u>
in an electrical circuit. It's given by this formula:

2) So, the potential difference across an electrical
component is the <u>work done</u> by that electrical
component (e.g. to light and heat energy by a bulb)
<u>per unit of charge</u>.

$$\text{P.D. (V)} = \frac{\text{Energy Transferred (E)}}{\text{Charge (Q)}}$$

3) <u>Voltage</u> and <u>potential difference</u> mean the <u>same thing</u>.
You can use <u>either</u> in your exam and scoop up the marks (so long as you use it <u>correctly</u>).

I think it's about time you took charge...

Don't get confused by the words <u>voltage</u> and <u>potential difference</u> — they mean the <u>same thing</u>. Just remember
that the potential difference is the energy transferred between two points in a circuit, per unit of charge.
Get those two formulas learned as well — examiners just love to test whether you understand them.

Circuits — The Basics

Formulas are mighty pretty and all, but you might have to design some <u>electrical circuits</u> as well one day. For that you're gonna need <u>circuit symbols</u>. Well, would you look at that... they're on this page.

Circuit Symbols *You Should Know* — Learn Them Well

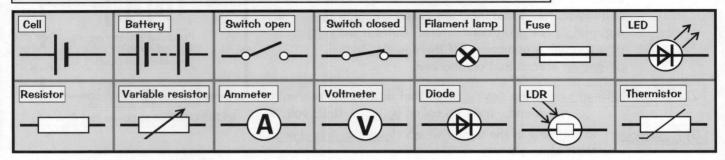

| Cell | Battery | Switch open | Switch closed | Filament lamp | Fuse | LED |
| Resistor | Variable resistor | Ammeter | Voltmeter | Diode | LDR | Thermistor |

The Standard Test Circuit

This is the circuit you use if you want to know the <u>resistance of a component</u>. You find the resistance by measuring the <u>current through</u> and the <u>potential difference across</u> the component. It is absolutely the most <u>bog standard</u> circuit you could know. <u>So know it</u>.

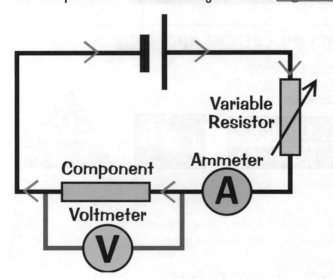

Variable Resistor

Component

Ammeter

Voltmeter

The *Ammeter*

1) Measures the <u>current</u> (in <u>amps</u>) flowing through the component.

2) Must be placed <u>in series</u> (see p. 71).

3) Can be put <u>anywhere</u> in series in the <u>main circuit</u>, but <u>never</u> in parallel like the voltmeter.

The *Voltmeter*

1) Measures the <u>potential difference</u> (in <u>volts</u>) across the component.

2) Must be placed <u>in parallel</u> (see p. 72) around the <u>component</u> under test — <u>NOT</u> around the variable resistor or the battery!

Six *Important Points*

1) This <u>very basic</u> circuit is used for testing <u>components</u>, and for getting <u>I-V graphs</u> from them (see next page).

2) The <u>component</u>, the <u>ammeter</u> and the <u>variable resistor</u> are all in <u>series</u>, which means they can be put in <u>any order</u> in the main circuit. The <u>voltmeter</u>, on the other hand, can only be placed <u>in parallel</u> around the <u>component under test</u>, as shown. Anywhere else is a definite <u>no-no</u>.

3) <u>Increasing (or decreasing) the resistance</u> of the variable resistor <u>decreases (or increases) the current</u> flowing through the circuit.

4) As the current changes, the <u>potential difference</u> across the component changes.

5) This allows you to take several <u>pairs of readings</u> from the <u>ammeter</u> and <u>voltmeter</u>.

6) You can then <u>plot</u> these values for <u>current</u> and <u>voltage</u> on a <u>I-V graph</u> and find the <u>resistance</u>.

A voltmeter has a very high resistance, so if you place it in series in the circuit, pretty much no current will be able to flow.

Measure gymnastics — use a vaultmeter...

The funny thing is — the <u>electrons</u> in circuits actually move from <u>−ve to +ve</u>... but scientists always think of <u>current</u> as flowing from <u>+ve to −ve</u>. Basically it's just because that's how the <u>early physicists</u> thought of it (before they found out about the electrons), and now it's become <u>convention</u>.

Resistance and V = I × R

With your current and your potential difference measured, you can now make some _sweet_ graphs...

Three _Hideously Important_ Current-Potential Difference (I-V) Graphs

I-V graphs show how the _current_ varies as you _change_ the _potential difference_ (P.D.). Learn these three real well:

Different Resistors

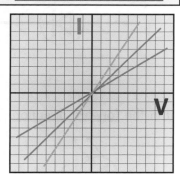

The current through a _resistor_ (at constant temperature) is _directly proportional to P.D._ _Different resistors_ have different _resistances_, hence the different _slopes_.

Filament Lamp

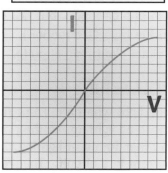

As the _temperature_ of the filament _increases_, the _resistance increases_, hence the _curve_.

Diode

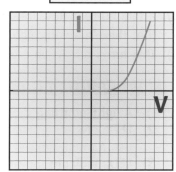

Current will only flow through a diode _in one direction_, as shown. The diode has very _high resistance_ in the opposite direction.

Resistance Increases with Temperature

1) When an electrical charge flows through a resistor, some of the electrical energy is _transferred to heat energy_ and the resistor gets _hot_.

2) This heat energy causes the _ions_ in the resistor to _vibrate more_. With the ions jiggling around it's _more difficult_ for the charge-carrying electrons to get through the resistor — the _current can't flow_ as easily and the _resistance increases_.

Resistance, Potential Difference and Current: V = I × R

Potential Difference = Current × Resistance

For the _straight-line graphs_ above, the resistance of the component is _steady_ and is equal to the _inverse_ of the _gradient_ of the line, or "_1/gradient_". In other words, the _steeper_ the graph the _lower_ the resistance.

If the graph _curves_, it means the resistance is _changing_. In that case R can be found for any point by taking the _pair of values_ (V, I) from the graph and sticking them in the formula _R = V/I_. Easy.

EXAMPLE: Voltmeter V reads 6 V and resistor R is 4 Ω. What is the current through Ammeter A?

ANSWER: Use the formula triangle for V = I × R. We need to find I, so the version we need is I = V/R. The answer is then: I = 6 ÷ 4 = 1.5 A.

In the end you'll have to learn this — resistance is futile...

You have to be able to _interpret_ current-potential difference graphs for your exam. Remember — the _steeper_ the _slope_, the _lower_ the _resistance_. And you need to know that formula inside out, back to front, upside down and in Swahili. It's the most important equation in electrics, bar none. (P.S. I might let you off the Swahili.)

Section Four — Electricity

Circuit Devices

You might consider yourself a bit of an <u>expert</u> in circuit components — you're enlightened about bulbs, you're switched on to switches... Just make sure you know these ones as well — they're a <u>little bit trickier</u>.

Current Only Flows in One Direction through a Diode

1) A diode is a special device made from <u>semiconductor</u> material such as <u>silicon</u>.
2) It is used to <u>regulate</u> the <u>potential difference</u> in circuits.
3) It lets current flow freely through it in <u>one direction</u>, but <u>not</u> in the other (i.e. there's a very high resistance in the <u>reverse</u> direction).
4) This turns out to be real useful in various <u>electronic circuits</u>.

Light-Emitting Diodes are Very Useful

1) A <u>light-emitting diode</u> (LED) emits light when a current flows through it in the <u>forward direction</u>.
2) LEDs are being used more and more as lighting, as they use a much <u>smaller current</u> than other forms of lighting.
3) LEDs indicate the presence of current in a circuit. They're often used in appliances (e.g. TVs) to show that they are <u>switched on</u>.
4) They're also used in <u>digital clocks</u>, <u>traffic lights</u> and <u>remote controls</u>.

Diodes Can be Used to Rectify Alternating Current

<u>Mains electricity</u> supplies <u>alternating current</u> (AC, current that changes direction), but many devices need <u>direct current</u> (DC, current that only flows in one direction). So we need a way of turning (<u>rectifying</u>) AC into DC. <u>Diodes</u> are used:

A single diode only lets through current in half of the cycle. This is called <u>half wave rectification</u>.

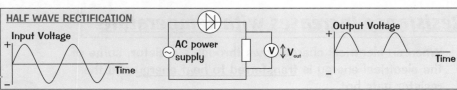

A Light-Dependent Resistor or "LDR" to You

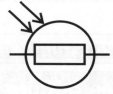

1) An LDR is a resistor that is <u>dependent</u> on the <u>intensity</u> of <u>light</u>. Simple really.
2) In <u>bright light</u>, the resistance <u>falls</u>.
3) In <u>darkness</u>, the resistance is <u>highest</u>.
4) They have lots of applications including <u>automatic night lights</u>, outdoor lighting and <u>burglar detectors</u>.

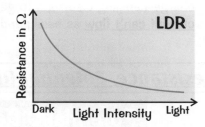

The Resistance of a Thermistor Decreases as Temperature Increases

1) A <u>thermistor</u> is a <u>temperature-dependent</u> resistor.
2) In <u>hot</u> conditions, the resistance <u>drops</u>.
3) In <u>cool</u> conditions, the resistance goes <u>up</u>.
4) Thermistors make useful <u>temperature detectors</u>, e.g. <u>car engine</u> temperature sensors and electronic <u>thermostats</u>.

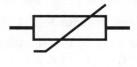
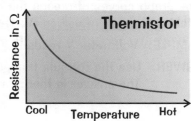

LDRs — Light-Dependent Robbers...

LDRs are good triggers in security systems, because they can detect when the <u>light intensity</u> changes. So if a robber walks in front of a <u>beam of light</u> pointed at the LDR, the <u>resistance shoots up</u> and an alarm goes off.

Series Circuits

You need to be able to tell the difference between series and parallel circuits <u>just by looking at them</u>.
You also need to know the <u>rules</u> about what happens with both types. Read on.

Series Circuits — All or Nothing

1) In <u>series circuits</u>, the different components are connected <u>in a line</u>, <u>end to end</u>, between the +ve and –ve of the power supply (except for <u>voltmeters</u>, which are always connected <u>in parallel</u>, but they don't count as part of the circuit).

2) If you remove or disconnect <u>one</u> component, the circuit is <u>broken</u> and they all <u>stop</u>.

3) This is generally <u>not very handy</u>, and in practice <u>very few things</u> are connected in series.

1) Potential Difference is Shared:

In series circuits the <u>total P.D.</u> of the <u>supply</u> is <u>shared</u> between the various <u>components</u>. So the <u>voltages</u> round a series circuit <u>always add up</u> to equal the <u>source voltage</u>:

$$V = V_1 + V_2 + ...$$

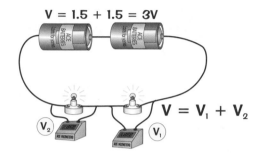

2) Current is the Same Everywhere:

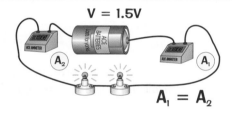

$V = 1.5V$

$A_1 = A_2$

1) In series circuits the <u>same current</u> flows through <u>all parts</u> of the circuit, i.e:

$$A_1 = A_2$$

2) The <u>size</u> of the current is determined by the <u>total P.D.</u> of the cells and the <u>total resistance</u> of the circuit: i.e. $I = V/R$

3) Resistance Adds Up:

1) In series circuits the <u>total resistance</u> is just the <u>sum</u> of all the resistances:

$$R = R_1 + R_2 + R_3$$

2) The <u>bigger</u> the <u>resistance</u> of a component, the bigger its <u>share</u> of the <u>total P.D.</u>

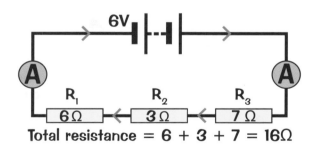

Total resistance = 6 + 3 + 7 = 16Ω

Cell Voltages Add Up:

1) There is a bigger potential difference when more cells are in series, provided the cells are all <u>connected</u> the <u>same way</u>.

2) For example when two batteries of voltage 1.5 V are <u>connected in series</u> they supply **3 V** <u>between them</u>.

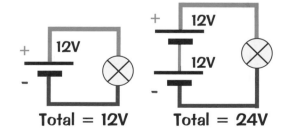

Total = 12V   Total = 24V

Series circuits — they're no laughing matter...

If you connect a lamp to a battery, it lights up with a certain brightness. If you then add more identical lamps in series with the first one, they'll all light up <u>less brightly</u> than before. That's because in a series circuit the voltage is <u>shared out</u> between all the components. That doesn't happen in parallel circuits...

Parallel Circuits

Parallel circuits are much more sensible than series circuits and so they're much more common in real life. All the electrics in your house will be wired in parallel circuits.

Parallel Circuits — Independence and Isolation

1) In parallel circuits, each component is separately connected to the +ve and −ve of the supply.
2) If you remove or disconnect one of them, it will hardly affect the others at all.
3) This is obviously how most things must be connected, for example in cars and in household electrics. You have to be able to switch everything on and off separately.

1) P.D. is the Same Across All Components:

1) In parallel circuits all components get the full source P.D., so the voltage is the same across all components:

$$V_1 = V_2 = V_3$$

2) This means that identical bulbs connected in parallel will all be at the same brightness.

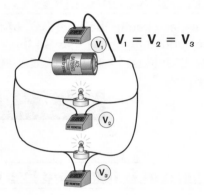

$V_1 = V_2 = V_3$

2) Current is Shared Between Branches:

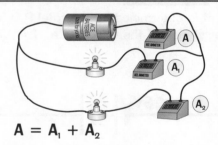

$A = A_1 + A_2$

1) In parallel circuits the total current flowing around the circuit is equal to the total of all the currents through the separate components.

$$A = A_1 + A_2 + ...$$

2) In a parallel circuit, there are junctions where the current either splits or rejoins. The total current going into a junction has to equal the total current leaving.

3) If two identical components are connected in parallel then the same current will flow through each component.

Voltmeters and Ammeters Are Exceptions to the Rule:

1) Ammeters and voltmeters are exceptions to the series and parallel rules.
2) Ammeters are always connected in series even in a parallel circuit.
3) Voltmeters are always connected in parallel with a component even in a series circuit.

A current shared — is a current halved...

Parallel circuits might look a bit scarier than series ones, but they're much more useful — and you don't have to learn as many equations for them (yay!). Remember: each branch has the same voltage across it, and the total current is equal to the sum of the currents through each of the branches.

Mains Electricity

Electric current is the <u>movement of charge carriers</u>. To transfer energy, it <u>doesn't matter which way</u> the charge carriers are going. That's why an <u>alternating current</u> works. Read on to find out more...

Mains Supply is AC, Battery Supply is DC

1) The UK mains supply is approximately <u>230 volts</u>.

2) It is an <u>AC supply</u> (alternating current), which means the current is <u>constantly</u> changing direction.

3) The frequency of the AC mains supply is <u>50 cycles per second</u> or <u>50 Hz</u> (hertz).

4) By contrast, cells and batteries supply <u>direct current</u> (DC). This just means that the current always keeps flowing in the <u>same direction</u>.

Electricity Supplies Can Be Shown on an Oscilloscope Screen

1) A <u>cathode ray oscilloscope</u> (CRO) is basically a snazzy <u>voltmeter</u>.

2) If you plug an <u>AC supply</u> into an oscilloscope, you get a '<u>trace</u>' on the screen that shows how the potential difference (voltage) of the supply changes with <u>time</u>. The trace goes up and down in a <u>regular pattern</u> — some of the time it's positive and some of the time it's negative.

3) If you plug in a <u>DC supply</u>, the trace you get is just a <u>straight line</u>.

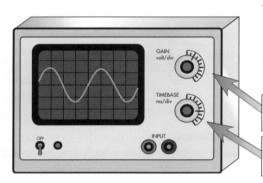

4) The <u>vertical height</u> of the AC trace at any point shows the <u>input voltage</u> at that point. By measuring the height of the trace you can find the potential difference of the AC supply.

5) For DC it's a <u>lot simpler</u> — the voltage is just the distance from the <u>straight line trace</u> to the centre line.

The GAIN dial controls how many volts each centimetre division represents on the vertical axis.

The TIMEBASE dial controls how many milliseconds (1 ms = 0.001 s) each division represents on the horizontal axis.

Learn How to Read an Oscilloscope Trace

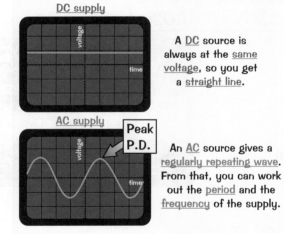

A <u>DC</u> source is always at the <u>same voltage</u>, so you get a <u>straight line</u>.

An <u>AC</u> source gives a <u>regularly repeating wave</u>. From that, you can work out the <u>period</u> and the <u>frequency</u> of the supply.

You work out the frequency using:

$$\text{Frequency (Hz)} = \frac{1}{\text{Time period (s)}}$$

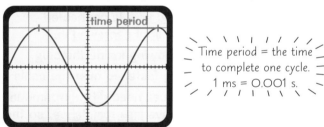

EXAMPLE: The trace below comes from an oscilloscope with the timebase set to 5 ms/div. Find: a) the time period, and b) the frequency of the AC supply.

Time period = the time to complete one cycle. 1 ms = 0.001 s.

<u>ANSWER</u>: a) To find the time period, measure the horizontal distance between two peaks. The time period of the signal is 6 divisions. Multiply by the timebase:
Time period = 5 ms × 6 = <u>0.03 s</u>

b) Using the frequency formula on the left:
Frequency = 1/0.03 = <u>33 Hz</u>

I wish my bank account had a gain dial...

Because mains power is AC, its current can be increased or decreased using a device called a <u>transformer</u>.
The lower the current in power transmission lines, the less energy is wasted as heat (see page 79 for more).

Electricity in the Home

Now then, did you know... electricity is <u>dangerous</u>. It can kill you. Well just watch out for it, that's all.

Hazards in the Home — Eliminate Them Before They Eliminate You

This is mostly <u>common sense</u>, but it won't hurt to learn these typical <u>electrical hazards</u> —
and it might hurt you if you don't....

1) <u>Long cables</u>.
2) <u>Frayed cables</u>.
3) <u>Cables</u> in contact with something <u>hot</u> or <u>wet</u>.
4) <u>Water near sockets</u>.
5) <u>Shoving</u> things into sockets.

6) <u>Damaged plugs</u>.
7) <u>Too many</u> plugs into one socket.
8) Lighting sockets <u>without bulbs in</u>.
9) Appliances without their <u>covers</u> on.

Most Cables Have Three Separate Wires

1) Most electrical appliances are connected to the mains supply by <u>three-core</u> cables. This means that they have <u>three wires</u> inside them, each with a <u>core of copper</u> and a <u>coloured plastic coating</u>.
2) The brown <u>LIVE WIRE</u> in a mains supply alternates between a <u>HIGH +VE AND –VE VOLTAGE</u>.
3) The blue <u>NEUTRAL WIRE</u> is always at <u>0V</u>. Electricity normally flows in and out through the live and neutral wires only.
4) The green and yellow <u>EARTH WIRE</u> is for protecting the wiring, and for safety — it works together with a fuse to prevent fire and shocks. It is attached to the metal casing of the appliance and <u>carries the electricity to earth</u> (and away from you) should something go wrong and the live or neutral wires touch the metal case.
5) The cables for some appliances only have two wires inside them — they <u>don't need</u> an earth wire. These are called <u>two-core cables</u>, and there's more on them on the next page.

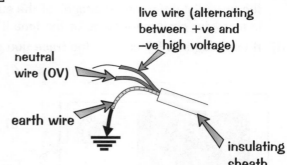

live wire (alternating between +ve and –ve high voltage)

neutral wire (0V)

earth wire

insulating sheath

Three-Pin Plugs and Cables — Learn the Safety Features

Get the Wiring Right

1) The <u>right coloured wire</u> is connected to each pin, and <u>firmly screwed</u> in.
2) <u>No bare wires</u> showing inside the plug.
3) <u>Cable grip</u> tightly fastened over the cable <u>outer layer</u>.
4) Different appliances need <u>different</u> amounts of electrical energy. <u>Thicker</u> cables have <u>less resistance</u>, so they carry <u>more current</u>.

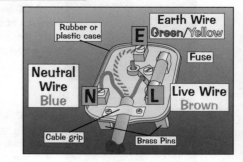

Rubber or plastic case

Earth Wire Green/Yellow

Fuse

Neutral Wire Blue

Live Wire Brown

Cable grip

Brass Pins

Plug Features

1) The <u>metal parts</u> are made of copper or brass because these are <u>very good conductors</u>.
2) The case, cable grip and cable insulation are made of <u>rubber</u> or <u>plastic</u> because they're really good <u>insulators</u>, and <u>flexible</u> too.
3) This all keeps the electricity flowing <u>where it should</u>.

CGP books are ACE — well, I had to get a plug in somewhere...

Pure water doesn't conduct electricity, but water (usually) has mineral salts dissolved in it. These carry the charge around really well, making it a <u>very good conductor</u>. So don't blow dry your hair in the bath, OK?

Fuses and Earthing

Questions about fuses <u>cover a whole barrel of fun</u> — electrical current, resistance, energy transfers and electrical safety. Learn this page and make sure you've got it sussed.

Earthing <u>and</u> Fuses <u>Prevent</u> Electrical Overloads

The earth wire and fuse (or circuit breaker) are included in electrical appliances for safety and work together like this:

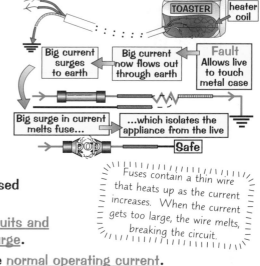

1) If a <u>fault</u> develops in which the <u>live wire</u> somehow touches the <u>metal case</u>, then because the case is <u>earthed</u>, <u>too great a current</u> flows in through the <u>live wire</u>, through the <u>case</u> and out down the <u>earth wire</u>.

2) This <u>surge</u> in current <u>melts the fuse</u> (or trips the circuit breaker in the live wire) when the amount of current is greater than the fuse rating. This <u>cuts off</u> the <u>live supply</u> and <u>breaks the circuit</u>.

3) This <u>isolates</u> the <u>whole appliance</u>, making it <u>impossible</u> to get an electric <u>shock</u> from the case. It also prevents the risk of <u>fire</u> caused by the heating effect of a large current.

Fuses contain a thin wire that heats up as the current increases. When the current gets too large, the wire melts, breaking the circuit.

4) As well as people, fuses and earthing are there to <u>protect the circuits and wiring</u> in your appliances from getting <u>fried</u> if there is a <u>current surge</u>.

5) <u>Fuses</u> should be <u>rated</u> as near as possible but <u>just higher</u> than the <u>normal operating current</u>.

6) The <u>larger the current</u>, the <u>thicker the cable</u> you need to carry it. That's why the <u>fuse rating</u> needed for cables usually <u>increases</u> with <u>cable thickness</u>.

Insulating Materials <u>Make Appliances "Double Insulated"</u>

All appliances with <u>metal cases</u> are usually "<u>earthed</u>" to reduce the danger of <u>electric shock</u>. "Earthing" just means the case must be attached to an <u>earth wire</u>. An earthed conductor can <u>never become live</u>. If the appliance has a <u>plastic casing</u> and no metal parts <u>showing</u> then it's said to be <u>double insulated</u>.

Anything with <u>double insulation</u> like that doesn't <u>need</u> an earth wire — just a live and neutral. Cables that <u>only carry</u> the <u>live</u> and <u>neutral</u> wires are known as <u>two-core cables</u>.

Circuit Breakers <u>Have Some</u> Advantages <u>Over</u> Fuses

1) <u>Circuit breakers</u> are an <u>electrical safety device</u> used in some circuits. Like <u>fuses</u>, they <u>protect</u> the circuit from <u>damage</u> if <u>too much</u> current flows.

2) When <u>circuit breakers</u> detect a <u>surge</u> in <u>current</u> in a circuit, they <u>break</u> the circuit by <u>opening</u> a <u>switch</u>.

3) A circuit breaker (and the circuit they're in) can easily be <u>reset</u> by flicking a <u>switch</u> on the device. This makes them <u>more convenient</u> than fuses — which have to be <u>replaced</u> once they've melted.

4) They are, however, a lot <u>more expensive</u> to buy than fuses.

5) One type of circuit breaker used instead of a fuse and an earth wire is a <u>Residual Current Circuit Breaker</u> (<u>RCCB</u>):

   a) Normally exactly the <u>same current</u> flows through the <u>live</u> and <u>neutral</u> wires. If somebody <u>touches</u> the live wire, a <u>small but deadly current</u> will flow <u>through them</u> to the <u>earth</u>. This means the <u>neutral wire</u> carries <u>less current</u> than the live wire. The RCCB detects this <u>difference</u> in current and <u>quickly cuts off the power</u> by opening a switch.

   b) They also operate much <u>faster</u> than fuses — they break the circuit <u>as soon as there is a current surge</u> — no time is wasted waiting for the current to <u>melt a fuse</u>. This makes them safer.

   c) RCCBs even work for <u>small current changes</u> that might not be large enough to melt a fuse. Since even <u>small current changes</u> could be <u>fatal</u>, this means RCCBs are more effective at protecting against electrocution.

<u>Why are earth wires green and yellow — when mud is brown..?</u>

All these <u>safety precautions</u> mean it's pretty difficult to get electrocuted on modern appliances. But that's only so long as they are in <u>good condition</u> and you're not doing <u>something really stupid</u>. Watch out for frayed wires, don't overload plugs, and for goodness sake don't use a knife to get toast out of a toaster when it is switched on.

Energy and Power in Circuits

Electricity is just another form of <u>energy</u> — which means that it is always <u>conserved</u>.

Energy _is_ Transferred _from Cells and Other_ Sources

Anything which <u>supplies electricity</u> is also supplying <u>energy</u>.

So cells, batteries, generators, etc. all <u>transfer energy</u> to components in the circuit:

| <u>Motion</u>: motors | <u>Light</u>: light bulbs | <u>Heat</u>: Hair dryers/kettles | <u>Sound</u>: speakers |

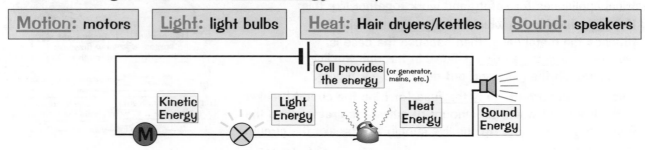

All _Resistors_ Produce _Heat_ When a _Current_ Flows Through Them

1) Whenever a <u>current</u> flows through anything with <u>electrical resistance</u> (which is pretty much everything) then <u>electrical energy</u> is converted into <u>heat energy</u>.

2) The <u>more current</u> that flows, the more heat is produced.

3) A <u>bigger voltage</u> means more heating because it pushes more current through.

4) <u>Filament bulbs</u> work by passing a current through a very <u>thin wire</u>, heating it up so much that it glows. Rather obviously, they waste a lot of energy as <u>heat</u>.

If an Appliance is _Efficient_ it _Wastes Less Energy_

All this energy wasted as heat can get a little <u>depressing</u> — but there is a solution.

1) When you buy electrical appliances you can choose to buy ones that are more <u>energy efficient</u>.

2) These appliances transfer more of their <u>total electrical energy output to useful energy</u>.

Not an energy efficient lamp.

3) For example, less energy is wasted as heat in power-saving lamps such as <u>compact fluorescent lamps</u> (CFLs) and <u>light emitting diodes</u> (p. 70) than in ordinary filament bulbs.

4) Unfortunately, they do <u>cost more to buy</u>, but over time the money you <u>save</u> on your electricity bills pays you back for the initial investment.

Power Ratings _of Appliances_

The total amount of energy transferred by an appliance depends on <u>how long</u> the appliance is on for and its <u>power</u>. The power of an appliance is the <u>rate</u> at which it <u>transfers energy</u>. Power is usually measured in <u>watts</u> (w) or <u>kilowatts</u> (kW).

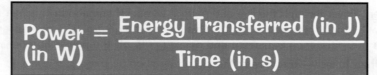

$$\text{Power (in W)} = \frac{\text{Energy Transferred (in J)}}{\text{Time (in s)}}$$

For example, if a kettle is on for 5 minutes and transfers 750 kJ in this time, the power of the kettle is 750 000 ÷ 300 = 2500 W = 2.5 kW. (750 kJ = 750 000 J, 5 minutes = 300 s.)

Ohm's girlfriend was a vixen — he couldn't resistor...

The equation for <u>power</u> is a real simple one, but it's <u>absolutely essential</u> that you've got it hard-wired into your memory. Remember: power is energy transferred per second. Power is energy transferred per second. Power is energy transferred per second...

Power and Energy Change

You can think about electrical circuits in terms of energy transfer — the charge carriers take charge around the circuit, and when they go through an electrical component energy is transferred to make the component work.

Electrical Power and Fuse Ratings

1) The formula for electrical power is:

   POWER = CURRENT × POTENTIAL DIFFERENCE

   $P = I \times V$

2) Most electrical goods show their power rating and voltage rating, which tell you the maximum power and voltage they can safely operate at. This normally relates to their operating power and voltage when they're plugged into the mains. To work out the size of the fuse needed, you need to work out the current that the item will normally use:

   EXAMPLE: A hair dryer is rated at 230 V, 1 kW. Find the fuse needed.
   ANSWER: I = P/V = 1000/230 = 4.3 A. Normally, the fuse should be rated just a little higher than the normal current, so a 5 amp fuse is ideal for this one.

The Potential Difference is the Energy Transferred per Charge Passed

1) When an electrical charge (Q) goes through a change in potential difference (V), then energy (E) is transferred.

2) Energy is supplied to the charge at the power source to 'raise' it through a potential.

3) The charge gives up this energy when it 'falls' through any potential drop in components elsewhere in the circuit.

   The formula is real simple:

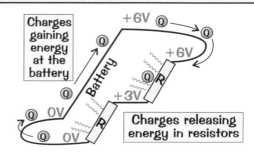

Charges gaining energy at the battery

Charges releasing energy in resistors

Energy transformed = Charge × Potential difference

$\dfrac{E}{Q \times V}$

4) The bigger the change in P.D. (or voltage), the more energy is transferred for a given amount of charge passing through the circuit.

5) That means that a battery with a bigger voltage will supply more energy to the circuit for every coulomb of charge which flows round it, because the charge is raised up "higher" at the start (see above diagram) — and as the diagram shows, more energy will be dissipated in the circuit too.

This is the same formula as the one you first saw on p.67.

EXAMPLE: The motor in an electric toothbrush is attached to a 3 V battery. If a current of 0.8 A flows through the motor for 3 minutes:

   a) Calculate the total charge passed.

   b) Calculate the energy transformed by the motor.

   c) Explain why the kinetic energy output of the motor will be less than your answer to b).

ANSWER: a) Use the formula (p.67) Q = I × t = 0.8 × (3 × 60) = 144 C

   b) Use E = Q × V = 144 × 3 = 432 J

   c) The motor won't be 100% efficient. Some of the energy will be transformed into sound and heat.

You have the power — now use your potential...

OK, another two formulas on this page. By this point you're probably experiencing a little bit of formula fatigue, but trust me, you'll be glad that you learned them. Try to think about exactly what each one means and how they work together — things are a lot easier to memorise if you have a real understanding of why they are there.

The Cost of Electricity

You can power all sorts of <u>toys and gadgets</u> with electricity. But it'll cost you.
'How much?' I hear you cry... Read and learn.

Kilowatt-hours (kWh) are "UNITS" of Energy

1) Electrical appliances <u>transfer</u> electrical energy into other forms,
   e.g. <u>sound</u> and <u>heat</u> energy in a <u>radio</u>.

> **ENERGY = POWER x TIME**
>
> This is just a rearrangement
> of the formula on p. 76.

2) The amount of <u>energy</u> that is transferred by an appliance
   depends on its <u>power</u> (<u>how fast</u> the appliance can transfer it)
   and the <u>amount of time</u> that the appliance is switched on.

3) Energy is usually measured in <u>joules</u> (J) — 1 J is the amount of energy transferred by a 1 W appliance in 1 s.

4) Power is usually measured in <u>watts</u> (W) or <u>kilowatts</u> (kW). A 5 kW appliance transfers 5000 J in 1 s.

5) When you're dealing with <u>large amounts</u> of electrical energy (e.g. the energy used by a home in one week),
   it's easier to think of the power and time in <u>kilowatts</u> and <u>hours</u> — rather than in <u>watts</u> and <u>seconds</u>.

6) So the standard units of electrical energy from the mains are <u>kilowatt-hours</u> (kWh) — <u>not joules</u>.

> A <u>KILOWATT-HOUR</u> is the amount of electrical
> energy used by a <u>1 kW appliance</u> left on for <u>1 HOUR</u>.

The Two Easy Formulas for Calculating the Cost of Electricity

These must surely be the two most <u>trivial and obvious</u> formulas you'll ever see:

> No. of <u>UNITS</u> (kWh) used = <u>POWER</u> (in kW) × <u>TIME</u> (in hours)

> Units = kW × hours

> <u>COST</u> = No. of <u>UNITS</u> × <u>PRICE</u> per UNIT

> Cost = Units × Price

> <u>EXAMPLE</u>: An electricity supplier charges 14p per unit.
> Find the cost of leaving a 60 W light bulb on for: a) 30 minutes   b) one year.
>
> <u>ANSWER</u>: a) <u>No. of units = kW × hours</u> = 0.06 kW × ½ hr = 0.03 units.
> <u>Cost = units × price per unit</u> (14p) = 0.03 × 14p = <u>0.42p</u> for 30 mins.
>
> b) <u>No. of units = kW × hours</u> = 0.06 kW × (24×365) hr = 525.6 units.
> <u>Cost = units × price per unit</u> (14p) = 525.6 × 14p = <u>£73.58</u> for one year.

> <u>EXAMPLE 2</u>: Each unit of electricity costs 14p. For how long can a 6 kW heater be used for 14p?
>   A 6 hours   B 1 hour   C 10 minutes   D 7 hours
>
> <u>ANSWER 2</u>: <u>The cost of 1 unit is 14p.</u> So for 14p you can use 1 unit.
> UNITS = POWER × TIME, so TIME = UNITS ÷ POWER = 1 ÷ 6 = 0.167 hours = 10 mins

You Need to Know How to Read an Electricity Meter

1) They might ask you to read values off an <u>electricity meter</u> in the exam — but don't worry,
   it's pretty straightforward. The units are usually in <u>kWh</u> — but make sure you <u>check</u>.

2) You could be given <u>two</u> meter readings and be asked to work out the <u>total energy</u>
   that's been used over a particular <u>time period</u>. Just <u>subtract</u> the meter reading at
   the <u>start</u> of the time (the <u>smaller</u> one) from the reading at the <u>end</u> to work this out.

> 1 3 5 9 2 . 3 2 kWh
> Electricity Meter

500 kWh doesn't mean much to anyone — £70 is far more real...

In <u>reality</u> most electricity suppliers have <u>complicated formulas</u> for working out the cost of electricity. Luckily in
the exam you'll just be told how much a particular energy supplier charges per unit or something, phew.

The National Grid

The <u>National Grid</u> is the <u>network</u> of pylons and cables that covers <u>the whole of Britain</u>, getting electricity to homes everywhere. Whoever you pay for your electricity, it's the National Grid that gets it to you.

Electricity _is Distributed_ **via the** National Grid...

1) The <u>National Grid</u> takes electrical energy from <u>power stations</u> to where it's needed in <u>homes</u> and <u>industry</u>.

2) It enables power to be <u>generated</u> anywhere on the grid, and then be <u>supplied</u> anywhere else on the grid.

3) To transmit the <u>huge</u> amount of <u>power</u> needed, you need either a <u>high voltage</u> or a <u>high current</u>.

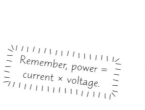
Remember, power = current × voltage.

4) The <u>problem</u> with a <u>high current</u> is that you lose <u>loads of energy</u> through <u>heat</u> in the cables.

5) It's much <u>cheaper</u> to <u>increase</u> the <u>voltage</u>. So before the electricity is sent round the country, the voltage is transformed to <u>400 000 V</u>. (This keeps the current very <u>low</u>, meaning <u>less</u> wasted energy because heating of the cables is <u>reduced</u>.)

Robots in disguise.

...With a Little Help from Pylons and Transformers

1) To get the voltage to 400 000 V to transmit power requires <u>transformers</u> as well as <u>big pylons</u> with <u>huge insulators</u> — but it's <u>still cheaper</u>.

2) The transformers have to <u>step</u> the voltage <u>up</u> at one end, for <u>efficient transmission</u>, and then bring it back down to <u>safe, usable levels</u> at the other end.

3) The <u>voltage</u> is <u>increased</u> ('<u>stepped up</u>') using a <u>step-up transformer</u>. (Yep, does what it says on the tin.)

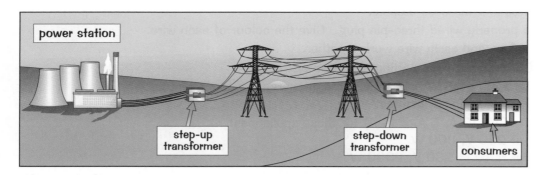

power station | step-up transformer | step-down transformer | consumers

You might be asked to identify or label these different parts of the National Grid.

4) To bring the voltage down to <u>safe usable levels</u> for homes, there are local <u>step-down</u> transformers scattered round towns — for example, look for a little fenced-off shed with signs all over it saying "Keep Out" and "Danger of Death".

5) This is the main reason why mains electricity is AC — so that the <u>transformers</u> work. Transformers <u>only work</u> on <u>AC</u>.

All that energy — straight down the grid...

Once power companies have <u>generated</u> electricity, they don't want to <u>waste it</u> by heating up miles and miles of power cables when they're <u>distributing</u> it. So they keep the <u>current</u> in the power cables <u>low</u>, and make the voltage <u>high</u>. Then the good folk of John o' Groats can still afford to boil the kettle. Problem solved.

Revision Summary for Section Four

Well done — you've made it to the end of another section. There are loads of bits and bobs about electricity which you have to learn. The best way to find out what you know is to get stuck into these lovely revision questions, which you're going to really enjoy (honest)...

1) What is current?
2) True or false: the greater the resistance of an electrical component, the smaller the current through it?
3)* 240 C of charge is carried through a wire in a circuit in one minute. How much current flowed in the wire?
4) What formula relates energy transferred, potential difference and charge?
5) Draw circuit symbols for:
   a) a cell, b) a battery, c) a fuse, d) a thermistor, e) an LDR.
6) Explain how you could find the resistance of a component. Draw a diagram of the circuit you would use.
7) Sketch typical current-potential difference graphs for:
   a) a resistor, b) a filament lamp, c) a diode. Explain the shape of each graph.
8) Explain how the resistance of a component changes with its temperature in terms of ions and electrons.
9)* What potential difference is required to push 2 A of current through a 0.6 Ω resistor?
10) True or false: a diode allows current to flow in both directions.
11) Give three applications of LEDs.
12) Diodes can be used to rectify AC. What does this mean?
13) Describe how the resistance of an LDR varies with light intensity. Give an application of an LDR.
14) Sketch a graph of resistance against temperature for a thermistor.
15)* A 4 Ω bulb and a 6 Ω bulb are connected in series with a 12 V battery.
   a) How much current flows through the 4 Ω bulb?
   b) What is the potential difference across the 6 Ω bulb?
   c) What would the potential difference across the 6 Ω bulb be if the two bulbs were connected in parallel?
16) What is the voltage of the UK mains supply? What is its frequency?
17)* An AC supply of electricity has a time period of 0.08 s. What is its frequency?
18)* An oscilloscope shows a trace of a DC supply. The gain of the oscilloscope is set to 5 V.
   If the trace is 4.5 vertical divisions above the centre line, what is the voltage of the supply?
19) Name the three wires in a three-core cable.
20) Sketch and label a properly wired three-pin plug. Give the colour of each wire.
21) Explain fully how a fuse and earth wire work together.
22) How does an RCCB stop you from getting electrocuted?
23)* Which uses more energy, a 45 W pair of hair straighteners used for 5 minutes,
   or a 105 W hair dryer used for 2 minutes?
24)* Find the appropriate fuse (3 A, 5 A or 13 A) for these appliances:
   a) a toaster rated at 230 V, 1100 W
   b) an electric heater rated at 230 V, 2000 W
25)* Calculate the energy transformed by a torch using a 6 V battery when 530 C of charge pass through.
26) What are the standard units of electrical energy from the mains?
27)* Electricity costs 17p per unit. A television is rated at 70 W.
   How much does it cost to watch television for two hours?
28) Why isn't electricity sent round the National Grid at a high current?
29) What do step-up and step-down transformers do?

* Answers on p. 100.

Magnets and Magnetic Fields

I think magnets is an <u>attractive</u> subject, but don't get <u>repelled</u> by the exam — <u>revise</u>.

Magnets *Produce* Magnetic Fields

1) All magnets have <u>two poles</u> — north and south.

2) A <u>magnetic field</u> is a <u>region</u> where <u>magnetic materials</u> (e.g. iron) experience a <u>force</u>. <u>Current-carrying wires</u> also experience a force acting on them (see page 83).

3) Magnetic fields can be represented by <u>field diagrams</u>.

4) <u>Magnetic field lines</u> (or "lines of force") are used to show the size and direction of magnetic fields. They <u>always</u> point from <u>NORTH</u> to <u>SOUTH</u>.

5) Placing the north and south poles of <u>two</u> permanent bar magnets <u>near</u> each other creates a <u>uniform field</u> <u>between</u> the two magnets.

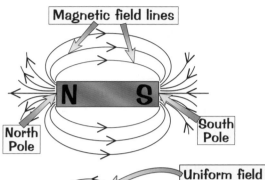
Magnetic field lines
North Pole
South Pole

Uniform field

You can use Compasses *and* Iron Filings *to look at* Magnetic Field Patterns

1) Compasses and iron filings <u>align</u> themselves with <u>magnetic fields</u>.

2) You can use <u>multiple compasses</u> to see the magnetic field lines coming out of a bar magnet or between two bar magnets.

3) You could also use iron filings to see magnetic field patterns. Just put the magnet(s) under a piece of paper and scatter the iron filings on top.

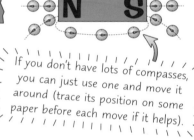

If you don't have lots of compasses, you can just use one and move it around (trace its position on some paper before each move if it helps).

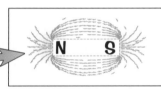

Magnetism *can be* Induced

1) Magnets affect <u>magnetic materials</u> and other <u>magnets</u>.

2) Like poles <u>repel</u> each other and opposite poles <u>attract</u>.

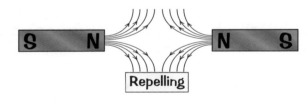
Repelling

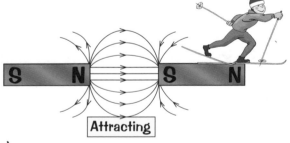
Attracting

3) Both poles <u>attract</u> magnetic materials (that aren't magnets).

4) When a magnet is brought <u>near</u> a magnetic material then that material acts as a <u>magnet</u>.

5) This magnetism has been <u>induced</u> by the original magnet.

6) The <u>closer</u> the magnet and the magnetic material get, the <u>stronger</u> the induced magnetism will be.

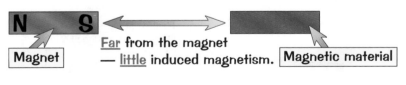
Magnet
<u>Far</u> from the magnet — <u>little</u> induced magnetism.
Magnetic material

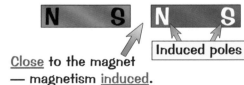
<u>Close</u> to the magnet — magnetism <u>induced</u>.
Induced poles

Magnets are like farmers — surrounded by fields...

Loads of really <u>useful</u> things work because of magnetism — compasses, headphones, computer hard drives, MRI medical scanners, mass spectrometers, those little magnets that hold your fridge door closed...

Electromagnetism

As you saw on the last page, magnetic fields exist around magnetic materials. Well, on this page you'll see that they're also found around a wire or conductor if you pass a current through them.

The Magnetic Field Round a Wire

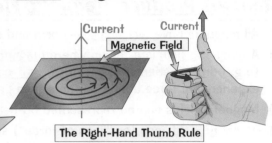

1) When a current flows through a wire, a magnetic field is created around the wire.

2) The field is made up of concentric circles perpendicular to the wire, with the wire in the centre.

3) Changing the direction of the current changes the direction of the magnetic field — use the Right-Hand Thumb Rule to work out which way it goes.

4) If you bend the wire into a flat circular coil, then the magnetic field in the centre is similar to that of a bar magnet. There are concentric ellipses (stretched circles) of magnetic field lines around the coil.

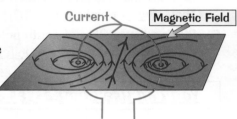

The Magnetic Field Round a Coil of Wire

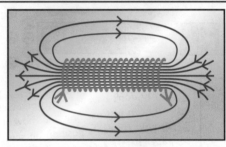

1) The magnetic field inside a coil of wire (a solenoid) is strong and uniform.

2) Outside the coil, the magnetic field is just like the one round a bar magnet.

3) If you stop the current, the magnetic field disappears. A magnet whose magnetic field can be turned on and off with an electric current like this is called an ELECTROMAGNET.

4) You can increase the strength of the magnetic field around a solenoid by adding a magnetically "soft" iron core through the middle of the coil.

A magnetically soft material magnetises and demagnetises very easily. So, as soon as you turn off the current, the magnetic field disappears — the iron doesn't stay magnetised. This is what makes it useful for something that needs to be able to switch its magnetism on and off (see below).

Electromagnets are Useful as Their Magnetism can be Switched Off

An electromagnet must be constantly supplied with current — as that's what produces the magnetic field. So if the current stops, then it stops being magnetic. Magnets you can switch on and off are really useful.

1) Electromagnets are used in some cranes to attract and pick up things made from magnetic materials like iron and steel, e.g. in scrap yards and steelworks.

2) Using an electromagnet means the magnet can be switched on when you want to pick stuff up, then switched off when you want to drop it. Which is useful.

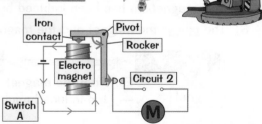

3) Electromagnets can also be used within other circuits to act as switches (e.g. in the electric starters of motors):

- When switch A is closed, it turns on the electromagnet, which attracts the iron contact on the rocker.

- The rocker pivots and closes the contacts turning on circuit 2.

I'm magnetically soft — I always cry when electromagnets are turned off...

Electromagnets pop up in lots of different places. For example, they're used in electric bells, car ignition circuits and some security doors. Electromagnets aren't all the same strength though — that wouldn't work. How strong they are depends on stuff like the number of turns of wire there are and the size of current going through the wire.

The Motor Effect

The <u>motor effect</u> can happen when you put a <u>current-carrying wire</u> in a <u>magnetic field</u>. It's really useful in stuff like... well... electric motors. If you want to know exactly what it is, you'll have to <u>keep reading</u>.

A <u>Current</u> in a <u>Magnetic Field</u> <u>Experiences a</u> <u>Force</u>

When a <u>current-carrying</u> wire is put between magnetic poles, the two <u>magnetic fields</u> affect one another. The result is a <u>force</u> on the wire. This can cause the <u>wire</u> to <u>move</u>. And it's called the <u>motor effect</u>.

This is an <u>aerial view</u>. The red dot represents a wire carrying current "out of the page" (towards you).

↑ Resulting Force

→ Normal magnetic field of wire
→ Normal magnetic field of magnets
→ Deviated magnetic field of magnets

1) To experience the <u>full force</u>, the <u>wire</u> has to be at <u>90°</u> to the <u>magnetic field</u>. If the wire runs <u>along</u> the <u>magnetic field</u>, it won't experience <u>any force at all</u>. At angles in between, it'll feel <u>some</u> force.

2) The force always acts in the <u>same direction</u> relative to the <u>magnetic field</u> of the magnets and the <u>direction of the current</u> in the wire.

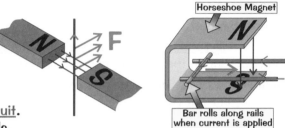

Horseshoe Magnet

Bar rolls along rails when current is applied

3) A good way of showing the direction of the force is to apply a current to a set of <u>rails</u> inside a <u>horseshoe magnet</u> (shown opposite). A bar is placed on the rails, which <u>completes the circuit</u>. This generates a <u>force</u> that <u>rolls the bar</u> along the rails.

4) The magnitude (strength) of the force <u>increases</u> with the strength of the <u>magnetic field</u>.

5) The force also <u>increases</u> with the amount of <u>current</u> passing through the conductor.

6) <u>Reversing</u> the current <u>or</u> the magnetic field also reverses the direction of the <u>force</u>.

<u>Fleming's Left-Hand Rule</u> <u>Tells You</u> <u>Which Way</u> <u>the Force Acts For</u> <u>Motors</u>

1) They could test if you can do this, so <u>practise it</u>.

2) Using your <u>left hand</u>, point your <u>First finger</u> in the direction of the <u>Field</u> and your <u>seCond finger</u> in the direction of the <u>Current</u>.

3) Your <u>thuMb</u> will then point in the direction of the <u>force</u> (<u>Motion</u>).

thuMb Motion — First finger Field — seCond finger Current

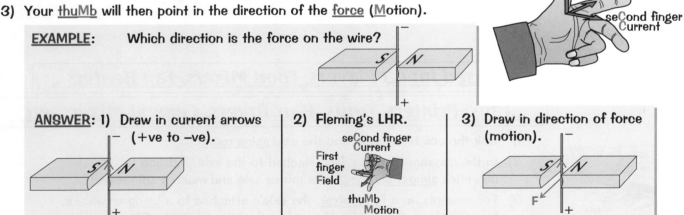

EXAMPLE: Which direction is the force on the wire?

ANSWER: 1) Draw in current arrows (+ve to –ve). 2) Fleming's LHR. 3) Draw in direction of force (motion).

<u>Remember the Left-Hand Rule for the motor effect — drive on the left...</u>

You're going to need to know the difference between left and right for this page. Learn the rule and <u>use it</u> — don't be scared of looking like a muppet in an exam. <u>Learn all the details</u>, diagrams and all, then cover the page and scribble it all down from memory. Then check back, see what you've missed, and try again.

The Simple Electric Motor

Electric motors use the motor effect (see previous page) to get them (and keep them) moving.
Read it. Understand it. Learn it. Lecture over.

The Simple Electric Motor

2 Factors which Speed it up:

1) More CURRENT
2) STRONGER MAGNETIC FIELD

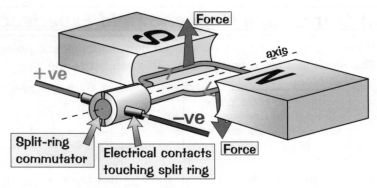

Force
axis
+ve
S
N
Split-ring commutator
Electrical contacts touching split ring
−ve
Force

1) The diagram shows the forces acting on the two side arms of the coil of wire.
2) These forces are just the usual forces which act on any current in a magnetic field.
3) Because the coil is on a spindle and the forces act one up and one down, it rotates.
4) The split-ring commutator is a clever way of "swapping the contacts every half turn to keep the motor rotating in the same direction". (Learn that statement because they might ask you.)
5) The direction of the motor can be reversed either by swapping the polarity of the direct current (DC) supply or swapping the magnetic poles over.

Direct current is current that only flows in one direction.

EXAMPLE: Is the coil turning clockwise or anticlockwise?

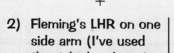

ANSWER:

1) Draw in current arrows (+ve to −ve).	2) Fleming's LHR on one side arm (I've used the right-hand arm).	3) Draw in direction of force (motion).

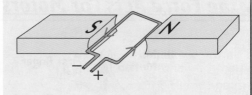

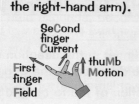

SeCond finger Current
First finger Field
thuMb Motion

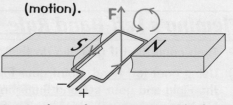

So — the coil is turning anticlockwise.

Electric Motors are used in: CD Players, Food Mixers, Fan Heaters...

...Fans, Printers, Drills, Hair Dryers, Cement Mixers, etc.

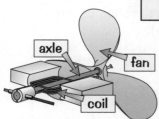

axle
fan
coil

1) Link the coil to an axle, and the axle spins round.
2) In the diagram there's a fan attached to the axle, but you can stick almost anything on a motor axle and make it spin round.
3) For example, in a food mixer, the axle's attached to a blade or whisks. In a CD player the axle's attached to the bit you sit the CD on. Fan heaters and hair dryers have an electric heater as well as a fan.

Hey, don't call my electric motor simple...

Those electric motors get everywhere. Life'd be much sadder without them and my hair would look even more ridiculous. It's all thanks to the motor effect. Make sure you know some appliances that use the motor effect and can describe how it helps to make each appliance work. It's the sorta thing that might be in an exam.

The Generator Effect

Electricity is generated using the <u>generator effect</u> (which is also known as <u>electromagnetic induction</u>). Sounds terrifying, but it isn't that complicated.

> **THE GENERATOR EFFECT:**
> The induction of a <u>**POTENTIAL DIFFERENCE**</u> (and maybe current) in a wire which is experiencing a <u>**CHANGE IN MAGNETIC FIELD**</u>.

(You'll sometimes hear it called the "<u>dynamo effect</u>".)

Moving a Magnet in a Coil of Wire Induces a Voltage

Potential difference is the same as voltage.

1) <u>The generator effect</u> creates a <u>potential difference</u> (and maybe a <u>current</u>) in a conductor. You can do this by <u>moving a magnet</u> in a <u>coil of wire</u> OR moving a conductor (wire) in a magnetic field ("cutting" magnetic field lines). Shifting the magnet from <u>side to side</u> creates a little "<u>blip</u>" of <u>current</u> if the conductor is <u>part of a complete circuit</u>.

A few examples of the generator effect:

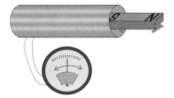 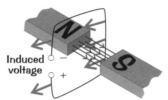 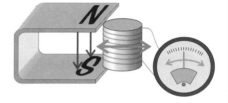

Induced voltage

2) If you move the magnet (or conductor) in the <u>opposite direction</u>, then the <u>voltage/current</u> will be <u>reversed</u>. Likewise if the <u>polarity</u> of the magnet is <u>reversed</u>, then the <u>voltage/current</u> will be <u>reversed</u> too.

3) If you keep the <u>magnet</u> (or the <u>coil</u>) moving <u>backwards and forwards</u>, you produce a <u>voltage</u> that <u>keeps swapping direction</u> — alternating current (<u>AC</u>).

You can create the same effect by <u>turning</u> a <u>magnet end to end</u> in a coil, or <u>turning</u> a <u>coil</u> inside a magnetic field. This is how <u>generators work</u> to produce <u>AC</u> or <u>direct current</u> (<u>DC</u>) — see next page.

1) As you <u>turn</u> the magnet, the <u>magnetic field</u> through the coil changes — this <u>change</u> in the magnetic field induces a <u>voltage</u>, which can make a <u>current</u> flow in the wire.

2) When you've turned the magnet through half a turn, the <u>direction</u> of the <u>magnetic field</u> through the coil <u>reverses</u>. When this happens, the <u>voltage reverses</u>, so the <u>current</u> flows in the <u>opposite direction</u> around the coil of wire.

3) If you keep turning the magnet in the <u>same direction</u> — always clockwise, say — then the voltage will keep on reversing every half turn and you'll get an <u>alternating current</u>.

Four Factors Affect the Size of the Induced Voltage

1) If you want a <u>different</u> peak voltage (and current) you have to change the rate that the <u>magnetic field</u> is <u>changing</u>. For a <u>bigger</u> voltage you need to <u>increase</u> at least one of these four things:

> 1) The <u>STRENGTH</u> of the <u>MAGNET</u>   2) The <u>AREA</u> of the <u>COIL</u>
> 3) The <u>number of TURNS</u> on the <u>COIL</u>   4) The <u>SPEED</u> of movement

2) To <u>reduce</u> the voltage, you would <u>reduce</u> one of those factors, obviously.

3) If you <u>turn</u> the magnet <u>faster</u>, you'll get a higher peak voltage, but also a <u>higher frequency</u> — because the magnetic field is reversing more frequently.

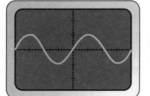 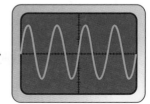

faster turns

The generator effect — works whether the coil or the field is moving...

"The Generator Effect" gets my vote for "Definitely Most Tricky Topic". If it wasn't so important maybe you wouldn't have to bother learning it. But this is how pretty much <u>all our electricity</u> is generated, so it's important.

Generators

Think about the simple electric <u>motor</u> — you've got a current in the wire and a magnetic field, which causes movement. Well, a <u>generator</u> works the <u>opposite way round</u> — you've got a magnetic field and movement, which <u>induces a current</u>.

AC Generators — Just Turn the Coil and There's a Current

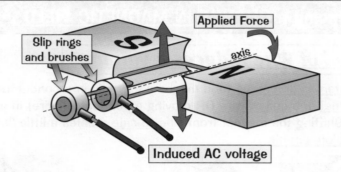

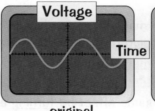 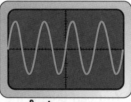

Fleming's <u>right-hand rule</u> is used for <u>generators</u> — the fingers mean the same thing as the left-hand rule for motors (p. 83), except the 2nd finger means induced voltage or current. Also, you need to use your right hand!

1) Generators <u>rotate a coil</u> in a <u>magnetic field</u> (or a magnet in a coil).
2) Their <u>construction</u> is pretty much like a <u>motor</u>.
3) As the <u>coil</u> (or <u>magnet</u>) <u>spins</u>, a <u>current</u> is <u>induced</u> in the coil. This current <u>changes direction</u> every half turn.
4) Instead of a <u>split-ring commutator</u>, AC generators have <u>slip rings</u> and <u>brushes</u> so the contacts <u>don't swap</u> every half turn.
5) This means they produce <u>AC voltage</u>, as shown by these <u>CRO displays</u>. Note that <u>faster revolutions</u> produce not only <u>more peaks</u> but <u>higher overall voltage</u> too.

A DC Generator Uses a Split-Ring Commutator

If you want to produce <u>DC</u> (direct current, which <u>doesn't</u> <u>change direction</u> every half turn) then you can use a DC generator. They're pretty simple, but <u>not used as often as AC generators</u> (the ones you get in <u>power stations</u>).

1) DC generators also <u>rotate a coil</u> in a <u>magnetic field</u> (or a magnet in a coil).
2) Their <u>construction</u> is pretty much exactly like a <u>motor</u>.
3) As the <u>coil</u> (or <u>magnet</u>) <u>spins</u>, a <u>current</u> is <u>induced</u> in the coil. This current <u>changes direction</u> every half turn.
4) DC generators <u>have</u> a <u>split-ring commutator</u>, (like the motor) so the contacts <u>swap</u> every half turn, keeping the induced current flowing in the <u>same direction</u> — i.e. it's <u>DC</u>.
5) This means they produce <u>DC voltage</u>, as shown by this <u>CRO display</u>. The line <u>isn't totally straight</u> like you've seen before for DC (see p. 73) but it's still only in one direction so it's DC.

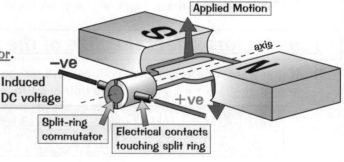

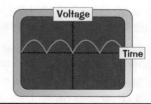

AC/DC — for those about to generate electricity, we salute you*...

The National Grid is fed by hundreds of <u>generators</u>. These are usually driven by <u>steam turbines</u> (and the steam usually comes from burning things). You can get small portable petrol generators too, to use where there's no mains electricity — on building sites, say. Don't forget you need to know about both types of generator.

Transformers

Transformers use the generator effect to change potential difference (p.d.). So they will only work on AC.

Transformers Change the p.d. — but only AC p.d.

There are different types of transformer. The two you need to know about are step-up transformers and step-down transformers. They both have two coils, the primary and the secondary, joined with a soft iron core.

STEP-UP TRANSFORMERS step the voltage up. They have more turns on the secondary coil than the primary coil.

STEP-DOWN TRANSFORMERS step the voltage down. They have more turns on the primary coil than the secondary.

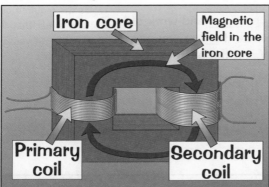

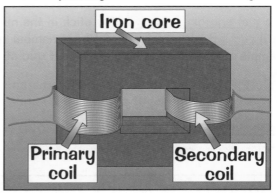

Transformers use the Generator Effect

1) The primary coil produces a magnetic field which stays within the iron core. This means nearly all of it passes through the secondary coil and hardly any is lost.

2) Because there is alternating current (AC) in the primary coil, the field in the iron core is constantly changing direction (100 times a second if it's at 50 Hz) — i.e. it is a changing magnetic field.

3) This rapidly changing magnetic field is then felt by the secondary coil.

4) The changing field induces an alternating potential difference across the secondary coil (with the same frequency as the alternating current in the primary) — electromagnetic induction of a potential difference in fact.

5) The relative number of turns on the two coils determines whether the potential difference induced in the secondary coil is greater or less than the potential difference in the primary.

6) In a step-up transformer, the p.d. across the secondary coil is greater than the p.d. across the primary coil.

7) In a step-down transformer, the p.d. across the secondary coil is less than the p.d. across the primary coil.

8) If you supplied DC to the primary, you'd get nothing out of the secondary at all. Sure, there'd still be a magnetic field in the iron core, but it wouldn't be constantly changing, so there'd be no induction in the secondary because you need a changing field to induce a potential difference. Don't you! So don't forget it — transformers only work with AC. They won't work with DC at all.

The Iron Core Carries Magnetic Field, Not Current

1) The soft iron core is purely for transferring the changing magnetic field from the primary coil to the secondary coil.

2) No electricity flows round the iron core.

The ubiquitous Iron Core — where would we be without it...

Transformers only work with AC. I'll say that again. Transformers only work with AC. Prevent disaster in the exam by remembering the fact that transformers only work with AC. Now that's out of the way, I recommend you learn the details and the diagrams, then cover the page and scribble them down.

Transformers

Ah, more about transformers. And as per usual, some equations to learn too. I don't like change.

The Transformer Equation — use it Either Way Up

You can calculate the output potential difference from a transformer if you know the input potential difference and the number of turns on each coil.

$$\frac{V_p}{V_s} = \frac{n_p}{n_s}$$

or

$$\frac{V_s}{V_p} = \frac{n_s}{n_p}$$

Potential Difference across Primary Coil	=	Number of turns on Primary Coil
Potential Difference across Secondary Coil		Number of turns on Secondary Coil

Well, it's just another formula. You stick in the numbers you've got and work out the one that's left. It's really useful to remember you can write it either way up. This example's much trickier algebra-wise if you start with V_s on the bottom...

It's the required output of a transformer that determines what input you give it (or the number of turns it has).

EXAMPLE: A transformer has 40 turns on the primary and 800 on the secondary. If the input potential difference is 1000 V, find the output potential difference.

ANSWER: $V_s/V_p = n_s/n_p$ so $V_s/1000 = 800/40$ $V_s = 1000 \times (800/40) = \underline{20\ 000\ V}$

Transformers are Nearly 100% Efficient So "Power In = Power Out"

The formula for power supplied is: Power = Current × Potential Difference or: $P = I \times V$.

So you can write electrical power input = electrical power output as:

$$V_p I_p = V_s I_s$$

V_p = p.d. across primary coil (V) V_s = p.d. across secondary coil (V)
I_p = current in the primary coil (A) I_s = current in the secondary coil (A)

EXAMPLE: A transformer in a travel adaptor steps up a 110 V AC mains electricity supply to the 230 V needed for a hair dryer. The current through the hair dryer is 5 A. If the transformer is 100% efficient, calculate how much current is drawn by the transformer from the mains supply.

ANSWER: $V_p \times I_p = V_s \times I_s$ so $110 \times I_p = 230 \times 5$ $I_p = (230 \times 5) \div 110 = \underline{10.5\ A}$

Switch Mode Transformers are used in Chargers and Power Supplies

1) Switch mode transformers are a type of transformer that operate at higher frequencies than traditional transformers.

2) They usually operate at between 50 kHz and 200 kHz.

3) They can be made much lighter and smaller than traditional transformers that work from a 50 Hz mains supply.

4) This makes them more useful in things like mobile phone chargers and power supplies, e.g. for laptops.

5) Switch mode transformers are more efficient than other types of transformer. They use very little power when they're switched on but no load (the thing you're charging or powering) is applied, e.g. if you've left your phone charger plugged in but haven't attached your phone.

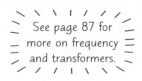

See page 87 for more on frequency and transformers.

Which transformer do you need to enslave the universe — Megatron...

You'll need to practise with those tricky equations. They're unusual because they can't be put into formula triangles, but other than that the method is the same — stick in the numbers. Just practise.

Revision Summary for Section Five

Let's check you've transformed all that revision into knowledge.
Unfortunately, there's only one way to check you know it all. Sorry.

1) Sketch a diagram showing the magnetic field produced by a bar magnet.

2) Sketch a diagram showing how you can produce a uniform magnetic field using two bar magnets.

3) Sketch the magnetic field produced by a current-carrying straight wire.

4) What is an electromagnet?

5) Describe one use of electromagnets. Explain why they're good for this job.

6) Describe what happens to a current-carrying wire when it is placed in a magnetic field.

7) Name two factors that increase the strength of the force on a current-carrying wire in a magnetic field.

8) Describe the three details of Fleming's left-hand rule. What is it used for?

9)* The diagrams show a simple electric motor. The coil is turning clockwise.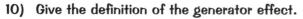
   Which diagram, A or B, shows the correct polarity of the magnets?

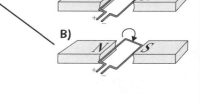

10) Give the definition of the generator effect.

11) Describe two ways in which you could induce a potential difference using a wire and a magnet.

12) Give four factors you could change to increase the size of an induced potential difference.

13) Describe how an AC generator works.

14) Describe how a DC generator works.

15) Sketch two types of transformer and explain the differences between them.

16)* An engineering executive is travelling from the USA to Italy and taking a computer monitor with him. In the USA, domestic electricity is 110 V AC, and in Italy it's 230 V AC. What kind of transformer would the engineering executive need to plug his monitor into?

17) Explain how a transformer works and why transformers only work on AC voltage.

18) Write down the transformer equation.

19)* A transformer has 20 turns on the primary coil and 600 on the secondary coil.
   If the input potential difference is 9 V, find the output potential difference.

20)* A transformer steps down 230 V from the mains supply to the 130 V needed for an appliance. If the transformer draws 2 A from the mains supply, calculate how much current goes through the appliance.

21) Give two advantages of switch mode transformers over traditional transformers.

* Answers on page 100.

Atomic Structure

The last section, hurrah! And what a section, Nuclear Physics — all the fun bits rolled up into one handy, revision-sized chunk...

Atoms — Nucleus in the Middle, Electrons Surrounding It

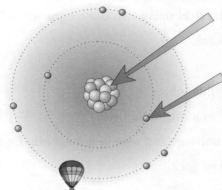

The nucleus is tiny but it makes up most of the mass of the atom. It contains protons (which are positively charged) and neutrons (which are neutral) — which gives it an overall positive charge.

The rest of the atom is mostly empty space. The negative electrons whizz round the outside of the nucleus. They give the atom its overall size — the radius of the atom's nucleus is about 10 000 times smaller than the radius of the atom. Crikey.

Learn the relative charges and masses of each particle:

PARTICLE	MASS	CHARGE
Proton	1	+1
Neutron	1	0
Electron	Very small ($1/2000$)	− 1

Number of Protons Equals Number of Electrons

1) Atoms have no charge overall.
2) The charge on an electron is the same size as the charge on a proton — but opposite.
3) This means the number of protons always equals the number of electrons in a neutral atom.
4) If some electrons are added or removed, the atom becomes a charged particle called an ion.

Isotopes are Different Forms of the Same Element

1) Isotopes are atoms with the same number of protons but a different number of neutrons.
2) Hence they have the same atomic number, but different mass numbers.
3) The atomic number or proton number is the number of protons in an atom.
4) The mass number is the number of protons + the number of neutrons in an atom.
5) Carbon-12 and carbon-14 are good examples of isotopes:

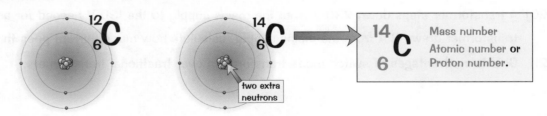

$^{12}_{6}C$ $^{14}_{6}C$

two extra neutrons

$^{14}_{6}C$ Mass number   Atomic number or Proton number.

6) Most elements have different isotopes, but there's usually only one or two stable ones.
7) The other isotopes tend to be unstable and radioactive, which means they decay into other elements and give out radiation.

Unstable isotopes — put them in a field...

So, it's the number of protons that decides what element something is. Then the number of neutrons decides what isotope of that element it is. Some isotopes of an element are stable, but others are unstable — it's the unstable ones that undergo radioactive decay and emit radiation. Which leads us nicely to the next page...

Radiation

You have just entered the subatomic realm — now stuff starts to get real interesting...

Radioactivity is a Totally Random Process

1) Radioactive substances give out radiation from the nuclei of their atoms — no matter what is done to them.
2) This process is entirely random. You can't say when it'll happen and you can't make a decay happen.
3) It's completely unaffected by physical conditions like temperature or by any sort of chemical bonding etc.
4) Radioactive substances spit out one or more of the three types of radiation: alpha, beta or gamma (p. 92).

Background Radiation Comes from Many Sources

Background radiation is radiation that is present at all times, all around us, wherever you go. It comes from:

1) Natural sources such as unstable isotopes found in rocks and radiation from space (cosmic rays).
2) Man-made sources, e.g. from nuclear weapons tests, nuclear accidents (e.g. Chernobyl) or nuclear waste.

Radiation Harms Living Cells

1) Alpha, beta and gamma radiation will cheerfully enter living cells and collide with molecules.
2) These collisions cause ionisation, which damages or destroys the molecules.
3) Lower doses tend to cause minor damage without killing the cell.
4) This can give rise to mutant cells which divide uncontrollably. This is cancer.
5) Higher doses tend to kill cells completely, which causes radiation sickness if a lot of body cells all get blasted at once.
6) The extent of the harmful effects depends on two things:
   a) How much exposure you have to the radiation.
   b) The energy and penetration of the radiation, since some types are more hazardous than others, of course.

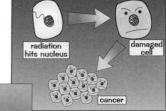

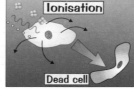

Outside the Body, β and γ-Sources are the Most Dangerous

This is because beta and gamma can get inside to the delicate organs, whereas alpha is much less dangerous because it can't penetrate the skin.

Inside the Body, an α-Source is the Most Dangerous

Inside the body alpha sources do all their damage in a very localised area. Beta and gamma sources are less dangerous inside the body because they mostly pass straight out without doing much damage.

Radioactive Materials Should be Handled Safely

Here are some precautions that should be taken when handling radioactive materials:

1) Use radioactive sources for as short a time as possible to keep exposure short.
2) Never allow skin contact with a source. Always handle with tongs.
3) Hold the source at arm's length to keep it as far from the body as possible.
4) Keep the source pointing away from the body and avoid looking directly at it.
5) Always store radioactive sources in a lead box and put them away as soon as the experiment is over.

Completely random — just like your revision shouldn't be...

People that work with radioactivity might wear lead aprons (attractive) and use lead screens for protection. And they sometimes wear photographic badges to detect how much exposure they have had. Safety first.

Ionising Radiation

Alpha (α) Beta (β) Gamma (γ) — there's a short alphabet of radiation for you to learn here. And it's all <u>ionising</u>.

Alpha Particles <u>are</u> Helium Nuclei

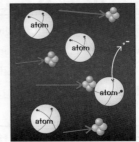

1) An <u>α-particle</u> is a <u>helium nucleus</u>, with a <u>mass</u> of 4 and a <u>charge</u> of +2.

2) They're made up of <u>two protons</u> and <u>two neutrons</u>.

3) So when a nucleus emits an <u>alpha particle</u> it forms a <u>new element</u> (see next page for more).

4) They are relatively <u>big</u> and <u>heavy</u> and <u>slow moving</u>.

5) They therefore <u>don't</u> penetrate very far into materials and are <u>stopped quickly</u>. They only have a <u>range</u> of about <u>5 cm</u> in <u>air</u>.

6) Because of their size they are <u>strongly ionising</u>, which just means they <u>bash into</u> a lot of atoms and <u>knock electrons off them</u> before they slow down, which creates ions — they're <u>ionising</u>.

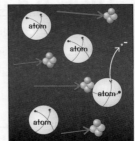

Beta Particles <u>are</u> Electrons

1) A <u>β-particle</u> is a fast-moving <u>electron</u> that comes from a nucleus.

2) Beta particles are <u>in between</u> alpha and gamma in terms of their <u>properties</u>.

3) They move <u>quite</u> fast and they are <u>quite</u> small (they're electrons).

4) They <u>penetrate moderately</u> into materials before colliding, have a <u>long range</u> in air (about 1 m), and are <u>moderately ionising</u> too.

5) For every <u>β-particle</u> emitted, a <u>neutron</u> turns to a <u>proton</u> in the nucleus (see next page for more).

6) Because a <u>β-particle</u> is simply an <u>electron</u> it has virtually no mass and a charge of –1.

Gamma Rays <u>are Very Short Wavelength</u> EM Waves

1) Gamma rays are the <u>opposite</u> of alpha particles in a way.

2) They <u>penetrate far into materials</u> without being stopped and pass <u>straight through air</u>.

3) This means they are <u>weakly</u> ionising because they tend to <u>pass through</u> rather than collide with atoms. Eventually they <u>hit something</u> and do <u>damage</u>.

4) Gamma rays are <u>electromagnetic waves</u> with <u>no mass</u> and <u>no charge</u>, which come from the nucleus.

5) Since a gamma ray is <u>just energy</u>, it <u>doesn't</u> change the element of the nucleus that emits it.

<u>Remember What</u> Blocks <u>the Three Types</u> of Radiation...

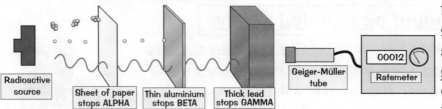

Radioactive source

Sheet of paper stops ALPHA | Thin aluminium stops BETA | Thick lead stops GAMMA

Geiger-Müller tube

00012

Ratemeter

1) <u>Alpha</u> is blocked by <u>paper</u>.

2) <u>Beta</u> is blocked by thin <u>aluminium</u>.

3) <u>Gamma</u> is blocked by <u>thick lead</u>.

<u>Similar</u> things block them — <u>skin</u> stops α, a thin sheet of <u>any metal</u> stops β, and <u>very thick concrete</u> stops γ.

If you popped a <u>radiation source</u> in <u>front</u> of <u>aluminium</u> then placed a <u>Geiger-Müller tube</u> behind it, and the ratemeter started <u>beeping</u> away, then that source would be <u>emitting gamma radiation</u>. Get it?

<u>I once beta particle — it cried for ages...</u>

When a nucleus decays by <u>alpha</u> emission, its <u>atomic number</u> goes down by <u>two</u> and its <u>mass number</u> goes down by <u>four</u>. <u>Beta</u> emission increases the atomic number by <u>one</u> (mass number <u>doesn't change</u>). But that's up next...

<u>*Ionising Radiation*</u>

<u>Balancing nuclear equations</u> — not as exciting as boogie-board balancing, but an important exam skill.

<u>**You Need to be Able to** Balance Nuclear Equations</u>

1) You can write alpha and beta decays as <u>nuclear equations</u>.
2) Watch out for the <u>mass and atomic numbers</u> — they have to <u>balance up</u> on both sides.

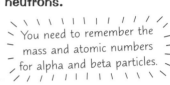

<u>*Alpha Radiation*</u>

1) An <u>α-particle</u> is a <u>helium nucleus</u> (<u>two protons</u> and <u>two neutrons</u>).
2) So, when a nucleus emits an <u>alpha particle</u>:
   - The <u>mass number decreases by 4</u> — because it <u>loses</u> two protons and two neutrons.
   - The <u>atomic number decreases by 2</u> — because it has <u>two less</u> protons.
   - It forms a <u>new element</u> — because the number of protons has <u>changed</u>.

   You need to remember the mass and atomic numbers for alpha and beta particles.

3) A typical <u>alpha emission</u>:

| mass number | $226 \longrightarrow 222 + 4 = 226$ |
| atomic number | $88 \longrightarrow 86 + 2 = 88$ |

<u>*Beta Radiation*</u>

1) A <u>β-particle</u> is a fast-moving <u>electron</u>.

   Beta particles can be written as $^0_{-1}e$ too.

2) So, when a nucleus emits a <u>beta particle</u>:
   - The <u>mass number doesn't change</u> — because it has <u>lost</u> a neutron but <u>gained</u> a proton.
   - The <u>atomic number increases by 1</u> — because it has <u>one more</u> proton.
   - It forms a <u>new element</u> — because the number of protons has <u>changed</u>.

   A neutron turns into a proton and a β particle (electron) is emitted.

3) A typical <u>beta emission</u>:

| mass number | $14 \longrightarrow 14 + O = 14$ |
| atomic number | $6 \longrightarrow 7 + (-1) = 6$ |

<u>**Alpha** and **Beta** **Particles** are **Deflected** by **Electric** and **Magnetic Fields**</u>

1) Alpha particles have a <u>positive charge</u>, beta particles have a <u>negative charge</u>.

2) When travelling through a <u>magnetic</u> or <u>electric field</u>, both alpha and beta particles will be <u>deflected</u>.

3) They're deflected in <u>opposite directions</u> because of their <u>opposite charge</u>.

4) Alpha particles have a <u>larger charge</u> than beta particles, and feel a <u>greater force</u> in magnetic and electric fields. But they're <u>deflected less</u> because they have a <u>much greater mass</u>.

5) <u>Gamma radiation</u> is an electromagnetic (EM) wave and has <u>no charge</u>, so it <u>doesn't get deflected</u> by electric or magnetic fields.

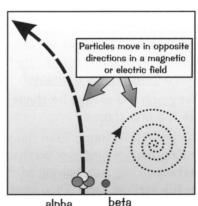

Particles move in opposite directions in a magnetic or electric field

alpha particle   beta particle

<u>*Sorry, no clear equations on this page...*</u>

The most important thing to remember is the symbol for each type of particle with its <u>atomic number</u> and <u>mass number</u>. As long as you know those, you should be able to write down an equation for alpha or beta decay.

Half-Life

The <u>unit</u> for measuring <u>radioactivity</u> is the <u>becquerel</u> (Bq). 1 Bq means <u>one nucleus decaying per second</u>.

The Radioactivity of a Sample Always Decreases Over Time

1) This is <u>pretty obvious</u> when you think about it. Each time a <u>decay</u> happens and an alpha, beta or gamma is given out, it means one more <u>radioactive nucleus</u> has <u>disappeared</u>.

2) Obviously, as the <u>unstable nuclei</u> all steadily disappear, the <u>activity</u> (the number of nuclei that decay per second) will <u>decrease</u>. So the <u>older</u> a sample becomes, the <u>less radiation</u> it will emit.

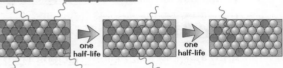

3) <u>How quickly</u> the activity <u>drops off</u> varies a lot. For <u>some</u> substances it takes <u>just a few microseconds</u> before nearly all the unstable nuclei have <u>decayed</u>, whilst for others it can take <u>millions of years</u>.

4) The problem with trying to <u>measure</u> this is that <u>the activity never reaches zero</u>, which is why we have to use the idea of <u>half-life</u> to measure how quickly the activity <u>drops off</u>.

5) Learn this <u>definition</u> of <u>half-life</u>:

6) In other words, it is the <u>time it takes</u> for the <u>count rate</u> (the number of radioactive emissions detected per unit of time) from a sample containing the isotope to <u>fall to half its initial level</u>.

> HALF-LIFE is the AVERAGE TIME it takes for the NUMBER OF NUCLEI in a RADIOACTIVE ISOTOPE SAMPLE to HALVE.

7) A <u>short half-life</u> means the <u>activity falls quickly</u>, because <u>lots</u> of the nuclei decay <u>quickly</u>.

8) A <u>long half-life</u> means the activity <u>falls more slowly</u> because <u>most</u> of the nuclei don't decay <u>for a long time</u> — they just sit there, <u>basically unstable</u>, but kind of <u>biding their time</u>.

Do Half-life Questions Step by Step

Half-life is maybe a little confusing, but exam calculations are <u>straightforward</u> so long as you do them slowly, <u>STEP BY STEP</u>. Like this one:

<u>A VERY SIMPLE EXAMPLE</u>: The activity of a radioisotope is 640 cpm (counts per minute). Two hours later it has fallen to 80 cpm. Find the half-life of the sample.

<u>ANSWER</u>: You must go through it in <u>short simple steps</u> like this:

INITIAL count:	(÷2)→	after ONE half-life:	(÷2)→	after TWO half-lives:	(÷2)→	after THREE half-lives:
640		320		160		80

Notice the careful <u>step-by-step method</u>, which tells us it takes <u>three half-lives</u> for the activity to fall from 640 to 80. Hence <u>two hours</u> represents three half-lives, so the <u>half-life</u> is 120 mins ÷ 3 = <u>40 minutes</u>.

Finding the Half-life of a Sample Using a Graph

1) The data for the graph will usually be <u>several readings</u> of <u>count rate</u> taken with a <u>G-M tube and counter</u>.

2) The <u>graph</u> will always be <u>shaped</u> like the one shown.

3) The <u>half-life</u> is found from the graph by finding the <u>time interval</u> on the <u>bottom axis</u> corresponding to a <u>halving</u> of the <u>activity</u> on the <u>vertical axis</u>. Easy peasy really.

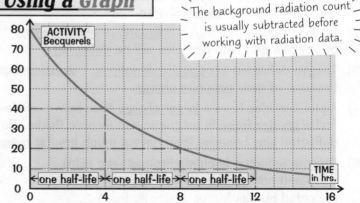

The background radiation count is usually subtracted before working with radiation data.

Half-life of a box of chocolates — about five minutes...

For <u>medical applications</u>, you need to use isotopes that have a <u>suitable half-life</u>. A radioactive tracer needs to have a short half-life to minimise the risk of damage to the patient. A source for sterilising equipment needs to have a long half-life, so you don't have to replace it too often (see next page).

Uses of Radiation

Radiation gets a lot of bad press, but the fact is it's essential for things like <u>modern medicine</u>. Read on chaps...

Smoke _Detectors_ — Use α-_Radiation_

1) A <u>weak</u> source of <u>alpha</u> radiation is placed in the detector, close to <u>two electrodes</u>.

2) The source causes <u>ionisation</u>, and a <u>current</u> flows between the electrodes.

3) If there is a fire then smoke will <u>absorb</u> the radiation — so the current stops and the <u>alarm sounds</u>.

Tracers _in Medicine_ — **Always** _Short Half-Life_ β **or** γ -_Emitters_

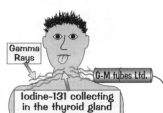

1) Certain <u>radioactive isotopes</u> can be <u>injected</u> into people (or they can just <u>swallow</u> them) and their progress <u>around the body</u> can be followed using an external <u>detector</u>. A computer converts the reading to a <u>display</u> showing where the <u>strongest reading</u> is coming from.

2) A well-known example is the use of <u>iodine-131</u>, which is absorbed by the <u>thyroid gland</u> just like normal iodine-127, but it gives out <u>radiation</u> which can be <u>detected</u> to indicate whether the thyroid gland is <u>taking in iodine</u> as it should.

3) <u>All isotopes</u> which are taken <u>into the body</u> must be GAMMA or BETA emitters (never alpha), so that the radiation <u>passes out of the body</u> — and they should only last <u>a few hours</u>, so that the radioactivity inside the patient <u>quickly disappears</u> (i.e. they should have a <u>short half-life</u>).

Radiotherapy — **the** _Treatment_ **of** _Cancer_ **Using** γ-_Rays_

1) Since high doses of gamma rays will <u>kill all living cells</u>, they can be used to <u>treat cancers</u>.

2) The gamma rays have to be <u>directed carefully</u> and at just the right <u>dosage</u> so as to kill the <u>cancer cells</u> without damaging too many <u>normal cells</u>.

3) However, a <u>fair bit of damage</u> is <u>inevitably</u> done to <u>normal cells</u>, which makes the patient feel <u>very ill</u>. But if the cancer is <u>successfully killed off</u> in the end, then it's worth it.

Sterilisation _of_ Food _and_ Surgical Instruments _Using_ γ -Rays

1) <u>Food</u> can be exposed to a <u>high dose</u> of <u>gamma rays</u> which will <u>kill</u> all <u>microbes</u>, keeping the food <u>fresh for longer</u>.

2) <u>Medical instruments</u> can be <u>sterilised</u> in just the same way, rather than by <u>boiling them</u>.

3) The great <u>advantage</u> of <u>irradiation</u> over boiling is that it doesn't involve <u>high temperatures</u>, so things like <u>fresh apples</u> or <u>plastic</u> <u>instruments</u> can be totally <u>sterilised</u> without <u>damaging</u> them.

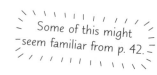
Some of this might seem familiar from p. 42.

4) The food is <u>not</u> radioactive afterwards, so it's <u>perfectly safe</u> to eat.

5) The isotope used for this needs to be a <u>very strong</u> emitter of <u>gamma rays</u> with a <u>reasonably long</u> <u>half-life</u> (at least several months) so that it doesn't need <u>replacing</u> too often.

Ionising radiation — _just what the doctor ordered..._

Radiation has many important uses — especially in <u>medicine</u>. Make sure you know why each application uses a particular <u>isotope</u> according to its half-life and the type of radiation it gives out.

Nuclear Fission and Fusion

Unstable isotopes aren't just good for medicine — with the right set-up you can generate some serious energy.

Nuclear Fission — the Splitting Up of Big Atomic Nuclei

Nuclear power stations generate electricity using nuclear reactors.
In a nuclear reactor, a controlled chain reaction takes place in
which atomic nuclei split up and release energy in the form of heat.
This heat is then simply used to heat water to make steam, which is
used to drive a steam turbine connected to an electricity generator.
The "fuel" that's split is usually uranium-235,
though sometimes it's plutonium-239 (or both).

The Chain Reactions:

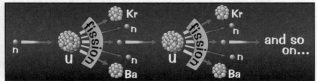

1) For nuclear fission to happen, a slow moving neutron must be absorbed into a uranium or plutonium nucleus. This addition of a neutron makes the nucleus unstable, causing it to split.

2) Each time a uranium or plutonium nucleus splits up, it spits out two or three neutrons, one of which might hit another nucleus, causing it to split also, and thus keeping the chain reaction going.

3) When a large atom splits in two it will form two new smaller nuclei. These new nuclei are usually radioactive because they have the "wrong" number of neutrons in them.

4) A nucleus splitting (called a fission) gives out a lot of energy — lots more energy than you get from any chemical reaction. Nuclear processes release much more energy than chemical processes do. That's why nuclear bombs are so much more powerful than ordinary bombs (which rely on chemical reactions).

Nuclear Fusion — the Joining of Small Atomic Nuclei

1) Two nuclei (e.g. hydrogen) can join to create a larger nucleus — this is called nuclear fusion.

2) Fusion releases a lot of energy (more than fission for a given mass) — all the energy released in stars comes from fusion.

3) But fusion requires really high temperatures (at least 10 000 000 °C) and pressures (which, handily, are found inside stars — see next page).

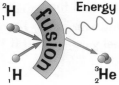

All the Natural Elements were Produced by Nuclear Fusion

1) The high temperatures and pressures inside stars cause different nuclei to fuse together.

2) The early Universe only contained hydrogen, but now it contains loads of different elements.

3) Loads of helium was created just after the 'Big Bang'. Then other elements formed as stars started to form and go through their different life cycles (see next page). Temperatures and pressures got high enough for other heavier elements to be created by nuclear fusion.

4) These other elements were distributed all over the Universe when stars exploded (supernovas).

Ten million degrees — that's hot...

Some people are trying to develop nuclear fusion reactors to generate electricity. It'd be great if we could get it to work — there's loads of fuel available and it doesn't create much radioactive waste compared with fission. But currently we need to use more energy to create the conditions for it than we can get out of it. Dawg-gone-it.

Section Six — Nuclear Physics

The Life Cycle of Stars

Stars go through <u>many traumatic stages</u> in their lives — just like teenagers.

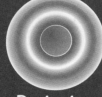

Protostar

1) Stars <u>initially form</u> from <u>clouds of DUST AND GAS</u>. The <u>force of gravity</u> makes the gas and dust <u>spiral in together</u> to form a <u>protostar</u>.

2) <u>Gravitational energy</u> is converted into <u>heat energy</u>, so the <u>temperature rises</u>. When the temperature gets <u>high enough</u>, <u>hydrogen nuclei</u> undergo <u>nuclear fusion</u> to form <u>helium nuclei</u> and give out massive amounts of <u>heat and light</u>. A star is born. Smaller masses of gas and dust may also pull together to make <u>planets</u> that orbit the star.

Main Sequence Star

3) The star immediately enters a <u>long stable period</u>, where the <u>heat created</u> by the nuclear fusion provides an <u>outward pressure</u> to <u>balance</u> the <u>force of gravity</u> pulling everything <u>inwards</u>. The star maintains its energy output for <u>millions of years</u> due to the <u>massive amounts of hydrogen</u> it consumes. In this <u>stable</u> period it's called a <u>MAIN SEQUENCE STAR</u> and it lasts <u>several billion years</u>. (The Sun is in the middle of this stable period — or to put it another way, the <u>Earth</u> has already had <u>half its innings</u> before the Sun <u>engulfs</u> it!)

Stars much bigger than the Sun

Stars about the same size as the Sun

4) Eventually the <u>hydrogen</u> begins to <u>run out</u>. <u>Heavier elements</u> such as iron are made by nuclear fusion of <u>helium</u>. The star then <u>swells</u> into a <u>RED GIANT</u>, if it's a small star, or a <u>RED SUPER GIANT</u> if it's a big star. It becomes <u>red</u> because the surface <u>cools</u>.

Red Giant

Red Super Giant

White Dwarf

5) A <u>small-to-medium</u>-sized star like the Sun then becomes unstable and <u>ejects</u> its <u>outer layer</u> of <u>dust and gas</u> as a <u>PLANETARY NEBULA</u>.

6) This leaves behind a hot, dense solid core — a <u>WHITE DWARF</u>, which just cools down to a <u>BLACK DWARF</u> and eventually disappears.

Supernova

Neutron Star...

...or Black Hole

7) <u>Big stars</u>, however, start to <u>glow brightly again</u> as they undergo more <u>fusion</u> and <u>expand and contract several times</u>, forming elements as <u>heavy as iron</u> in various <u>nuclear reactions</u>. Eventually they <u>explode</u> in a <u>SUPERNOVA</u>, forming elements <u>heavier than iron</u> and ejecting them into the universe to <u>form new planets and stars</u>.

8) The <u>exploding supernova</u> throws the outer layers of <u>dust and gas</u> into space, leaving a <u>very dense core</u> called a <u>NEUTRON STAR</u>. If the star is <u>big enough</u> this will become a <u>BLACK HOLE</u>.

Red Giants, White Dwarfs, Black Holes, Green Ghosts...

Don't forget — the life cycle of a star depends on its size. One that's similar in size to the Sun will eventually become a black dwarf. One much bigger than the Sun will explode in a supernova. Remember — the heaviest element produced in stable stars is iron, but it takes a <u>supernova</u> (or a lab) to create <u>the rest</u>.

Revision Summary for Section Six

There's some pretty heavy physics in this section. But just take it one page at a time and it's not so bad. You're even allowed to go back through the pages for a sneaky peek if you get stuck on these questions. Also, when this page is done, you're done — really well done, you're a physics champiooooooony, champiooooooony (olé, olé, olé, olé).

1) Draw a table stating the relative mass and charge of the three basic subatomic particles (protons, neutrons and electrons).

2) What happens to an atom to turn it into an ion?

3) Give the mass number and proton number of this isotope: $^{12}_{6}C$

4) True or false: radioactive decay can be triggered by certain chemical reactions?

5) Name the three types of radiation that radioactive substances can emit.

6) Why is radiation dangerous?

7) Which is the most dangerous form of radiation if you eat it? Why?

8) Describe the precautions you should take when handling radioactive sources in the laboratory.

9) What type of nucleus is an alpha particle: hydrogen or helium?

10) What type of subatomic particle is a beta particle?

11) List the properties of gamma radiation.

12) What substances could be used to block: a) alpha radiation, b) beta radiation, c) gamma radiation?

13) How does the mass number of a nucleus change after it's emitted: a) an alpha particle, b) a beta particle?

14) How does the atomic number of a nucleus change after it's emitted:

a) an alpha particle, b) a beta particle?

15)* Complete the following nuclear equations by working out the missing numbers shown by the dotted lines:

a) $^{131}_{53}I \rightarrow {}^{...}_{...}Xe + {}^{0}_{-1}\beta$ b) ${}^{...}_{...}Gd \rightarrow {}^{144}_{62}Sm + {}^{4}_{2}\alpha$

16) Sketch the paths of an alpha particle and a beta particle travelling through an electric field.

17) Give a definition of half-life.

18)* The activity of a radioactive sample is 840 Bq. Four hours later it has fallen to 105 Bq. Find the half-life of the sample.

19) Name one use of alpha radiation.

20) Give an example of how gamma radiation can be used in medicine.

21) Draw a diagram to illustrate the fission of uranium-235 and explain how the chain reaction works.

22) What is nuclear fusion?

23) Describe the steps that lead to the formation of a main sequence star (like our Sun).

24) Why will our Sun never form a black hole?

25) List the stages in the life cycle of a star much bigger than our Sun.

* Answers on p. 100.

Index

Answers

<u>Revision Summary for Section One (page 33)</u>

3) $a = (v - u) \div t$, so $a = (14 - 0) \div 0.4 = 35$ m/s^2

6) South is positive, North is negative.
So, 360 N $- 120$ N $= 240$ N south

8) $F = ma$, so $a = F \div m = 30 \div 4 = 7.5$ m/s^2

9) 120 N

15) Work done = force $\times$ distance.
$W = 535 \times 12 = 6420$ J

16) $E_p = m \times g \times h = 4 \times 10 \times 30 = 1200$ J

17) $E_k = \frac{1}{2} \times m \times v^2 = \frac{1}{2} \times 78 \times 23^2 = 20\,631$ J

18) E_k transferred = work done by brakes
$\frac{1}{2} \times m \times v^2 = F \times d$
$\frac{1}{2} \times 1000 \times 2^2 = 395 \times d$
$d = 2000 \div 395 = 5.1$ m
The car would come to stop in 5.1 m, so no,
he can't avoid hitting the sheep.

21) $P = (m \times g \times h) \div t$ ($g = 10$ N/kg)
$P = (78 \times 10 \times 20) \div 16.5 = 945$ W

24) $1.5 \times 600 = d \times 450$, so
$d = 900 \div 450 = 2$ m

26) $T = 1 \div f$, so $T = 1 \div 10 = 0.1$ s

28) $P = F \div A$, so $P = 20 \div 0.25 = 80$ Pa

<u>Wave Basics Top Tip (page 34)</u>

2375 m/s

<u>Revision Summary for Section Two (page 55)</u>

3) $v = f \times \lambda = 50\,000 \times 0.003 = 150$ m/s

10) $n = \sin i \div \sin r = \sin 12 \div \sin 8 = 1.49$

13) $n = \dfrac{1}{\sin C}$

$\sin C = 1 \div n = 1 \div 1.52 = 0.658$. So, $C = 41.1°$

26) $s = v \times t$, so $s = 1000 \times 0.00004 = 0.04$ m
so thickness of fat $= 0.04 \div 2 = 0.02$ m $= 2$ cm

28) Magnification = image height $\div$ object height
$= 6.0 \div 3.0 = 2$

31) Power = $1 \div$ focal length $= 1 \div 0.25 = 4$ D or m^{-1}

<u>Energy Transfer and Efficiency Top Tip (page 63)</u>

TV: 0.0318 or 3.18%, Loudspeaker: 0.0143 or 1.43%

<u>Revision Summary for Section Three (page 66)</u>

4) $E = m \times c \times \theta$, so $c = E \div (m \times \theta)$
$= 5000 \div (0.05 \times 40) = 2500$ J/kg°C

5) $E = m \times L_v = 0.5 \times 2\,260\,000 = 1\,130\,000$ J

20) Efficiency = Useful energy $\div$ Total energy
$= 70/100$ ($\times 100\%$) $= 0.7$ (70%)

21) a) 80 J   b) 20 J   c) 0.8 or 80%

22) Payback time = Initial Cost $\div$ Annual Saving
$= 4000/100 = 40$ years

<u>Revision Summary for Section Four (page 80)</u>

3) $I = Q \div t$, so $I = 240 \div (1 \times 60) = 4$ A

9) $V = I \times R$, so $V = 2 \times 0.6 = 1.2$ V

15) a) Current is the same everywhere in the circuit
and resistance adds up in a series circuit.
Total resistance $= 4 + 6 = 10\ \Omega$
$V = I \times R$, so $I = V \div R = 12 \div 10 = \underline{1.2\ A}$

b) Potential difference is shared between
the bulbs. $V = I \times R = 1.2 \times 6 = \underline{7.2\ V}$

c) In parallel, the potential difference is the same
across each branch of the circuit and is equal to the
supply potential difference, therefore the potential
difference across either bulb = $\underline{12\ V}$.

17) $f = 1 \div T$, so $f = 1 \div 0.08 = 12.5$ Hz

18) Voltage = gain $\times$ number of divisions
$= 5 \times 4.5 = 22.5$ V

23) P (in W) $= E$ (in J) $\div t$ (in s), so $E = P \times t$
Hair straighteners: $E = 45 \times (5 \times 60) = 13\,500$ J
Hair dryer: $E = 105 \times (2 \times 60) = 12\,600$ J
The hair straighteners use more energy.

24) $P = I \times V$, so $I = P \div V$
a) $I = 1100 \div 230 = 4.8$ A, so use a 5 A fuse.
b) $I = 2000 \div 230 = 8.7$ A, so use a 13 A fuse.

25) $E = Q \times V$, $E = 530 \times 6 = 3180$ J

27) No. of units = kW $\times$ hours $= 0.07 \times 2 = 0.14$ units
Cost = units $\times$ price per unit $= 0.14 \times 17$p $= 2.38$p

<u>Revision Summary for Section Five (page 89)</u>

9) A

16) Step-down

19) $V_s \div V_p = n_s \div n_p$ so $V_s = (600 \div 20) \times 9$
$= 30 \times 9 = 270$ V

20) $V_p \times I_p = V_s \times I_s$, so $I_s = (230 \times 2) \div 130 = 3.5$ A

<u>Revision Summary for Section Six (page 98)</u>

15) a) $^{131}_{53}\text{I} \rightarrow\ ^{131}_{54}\text{Xe} +\ ^{0}_{-1}\beta$

b) $^{148}_{64}\text{Gd} \rightarrow\ ^{144}_{62}\text{Sm} +\ ^{4}_{2}\alpha$

18) After one half-life the activity will be $840 \div 2 = 420$
Bq. After 2 half-lives, it will be $420 \div 2 = 210$ Bq.
After 3 half-lives, it will be $210 \div 2 = 105$ Bq.
This takes 4 hours, i.e. 3 half-lives = 4 hours.

So 1 half-life $= 4 \div 3 = 1\frac{1}{3}$ hours $= \underline{1\ \text{hr}\ 20\ \text{minutes}}$.